The Independent Hostel Guide 2020

England
Wales
Scotland
Northern Ireland

Edited by
Sam Dalley and Penny MacGregor

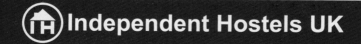

Independent Hostels UK

ISBN 978-0-9565058-9-7

Independent Hostel Guide 2020: England, Wales, Scotland & Northern Ireland. 29th Edition.

Editors: Sam Dalley and Penny MacGregor.

British Library Cataloguing in Publication Data. A catalogue record for this book is available at the British Library **ISBN 978-0-9565058-9-7**

Published by: Independent Hostels UK, Speedwell House, Upperwood, Matlock Bath, Derbyshire, DE4 3PE.
Tel: +44 (0) 1629 580427.

Printed by: Cambrian Printers www.cambrian-printers.co.uk

Front Cover Photo: Todor Tsvetkov © Istock

Back Cover Photos: Lockerbrook Farm Outdoor Centre pg 145 and The Lochside Hostel pg 335

Internal Photographs: Photo on page 358 credited to Brian Sutherland. Photo on page 362 credited to Ike Gibson. Photo on page 378 credited to Martin Thirkettle. Photo on page 232 credited to Mike Emmett. Photo on page 224 credited to Mick Garratt. Photos on page 205 credited to Rob Nobal. Photos on page 198 credited to Elliott Simpson. Photos on page 354 and 359 credited to VisitScotland/Paul Tomkins. Photos on page 333 credited to Allan Sutherland, Paul Higson, Colin McLean and Tom Daly. Photos on pages: 31,32,33,49,58,119,152,55,233,102,221,140,245,263,112,60,57,217,80,54,281,85,179,199,126,288,162,86,45,51,81,70,255,66,118,163,219,195 © National Trust / Ross Hoddinott, Joe Cornish, Sarah Bailey, Robert Morris, Mike Henton, Roy Jones, Alex Green, John Millar, Peter Muhly, Roger Coulam, Paul Harris, Graham Bettis, James Dobson, Andrew Butler, Stuart Cox, Paul Delaney, David Noton, John Malley, Drew Buckley, Tracey Willis, Rob Joules, Sarah Harris, Justin Seedhouse, Arnhel de Serra, David Sellman, Hywel Lewis, Chris Lacey, David Noton,Robin Sutton, John Miller, Peter Hall, Kevin Jones, Emily Vernon. **Other photos were donated by the accommodation and all copyright is retained.**

ISBN 9780956505897

9 780956 505897

Distributed in the UK by:
Cordee Ltd
Unit 11 Dodwells Bridge Industrial Estate
Hinckley , Leicestershire
LE10 3BS . Tel : 01455 611 185

CONTENTS

INDEPENDENT HOSTELS UK

Independent Hostels UK is a network of over 420 bunkhouses, hostels, camping barns and group accommodation centres. These provide a unique form of accommodation, ideal for groups, individuals and families who enjoy good company, independent travel and the outdoors.

Independenthostels.co.uk

INDEPENDENT HOSTELS

Independent hostels have shared areas, self-catering kitchens and bedrooms with bunks. They are great for group get-togethers and for those who enjoy the outdoors and independent travel. Bunkhouses, camping barns, boutique hostels, backpackers' hostels, bothies and outdoor centres are all types of independent hostel.

Self-catering facilities

Stays of one night or more

Private bedrooms, en suite rooms and dorms

Wild locations for outdoor activities

City centre locations for independent travel

Families, individuals and groups all welcome

Can be booked 'sole use' for get-togethers & groups

No membership requirements

95% are extra to the hostels in the YHA / SYHA

BEST PRICE GUARANTEE BEST PRICE

Booking.com, Hostelworld and Airbnb take up to 20% of your cash before passing it onto your hosts. You can stop this by booking direct on the hostels' own website. Our website, **independenthostels.co.uk** gives you access to the hostels' own websites and allows you to search over 420 sources of accommodation.

Independenthostels.co.uk where everything you pay and everything you say goes direct to your hosts.

The hostels and bunkhouses displaying the Best Price symbol on our website promise that you will get their accommodation at the lowest price if you book direct. For overseas see **www.bestprice-hostels.com**

KEY TO SYMBOLS

👫	**Dormitories**
🅿	**Private rooms (often ideal for families)**
🔺	**Sleeping bags required**
▦	**Hostel fully heated**
▦	**Some areas heated**
🚶	**Drying room available**
⠿	**Cooking facilities available**
🍴	**Meals provided or available locally**
((•))	**WiFi available**
Ⓢ	**Simple accommodation, basic, clean and friendly**
🐕	**Dogs by prior arrangement**
🚲	**Bike shed**
Ⓑ Ⓢ Ⓖ	**Bronze, Silver, Gold, Green Tourism Award**
🔺	**Affiliated to Hostelling International**
GROUPS ONLY	**Accommodation for groups only**
pp	per person
♿	**Some accessible areas (See Index pages 380-384)**

Independenthostels.co.uk

Follow our social media @indiehostelsUK for special offers.

IF YOU LIKE OUR GUIDE

Detailed information about each hostel / bunkhouse.

Large photos of the accommodation and detailed maps.

Online availability and a Direct Booking facility.

Links to the hostels' & bunkhouses' own websites.

Direct contact with the accommodation owners

Special Offers and Late Availability

Holiday ideas and magazine features to inspire you.

YOU WILL LOVE OUR WEBSITE

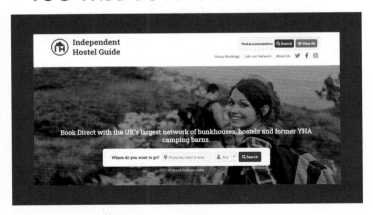

**Where everything you pay and
everything you say goes direct to your hosts.**

Independenthostels.co.uk

Cohort Hostel pg 44b

WHY BOOK DIRECT ?

Everything you pay goes to your hosts

You may get better rates

You can chat with the staff and discuss your needs

You may get preferential treatment

Book by email or phone, on the hostels own website or on independenthostels.co.uk

Independent Hostels UK is a network of accommodation owners. We are very different to online travel agents like Booking.com, Airbnb or Hostelworld who charge up to 20% in commission and service fees.

Our website provides a great selection of easily searched accommodation. When you place a booking on our website you are booking direct with your hosts and they get 100% of your money.

For a warm welcome, book direct

Independenthostels.co.uk/walking-festivals

15-19 April	Chepstow Walking Festival	Monmouthshire
24-26 April	Kington Walks Spring Weekend	Herefordshire
24-26 April	Galashiels Walking Weekend	Scottish Border
25 Apr-4 May	Ulverston Walk Fest	Cumbria
28 Apr-4 May	Settle-Carlisle Walking & Music Festival	Yorks/Cumbria
2-10 May	Haltwhistle Walking Festival	Northumberland
2-10 May	Ironbridge Gorge Walking Festival	Shropshire
8-10 May	Llangollen Walking Festival	N/E Wales
8-11 May	Kendal Walking Festival	Cumbria
10 May	Bingley Walking Festival	Yorkshire
15-17 May	Trefriw Walking Festival	Conwy
16-17 May	Farnham Walking Festival	Surrey/Hants
22-25 May	Drovers' Tryst Walking Festival	Perthshire
30 May-7 Jun	Gower Walking Festival	W Glamorgan
5-13 June	Annual South Downs Way Walk	E Sussex/Hants
12-21 June	Moray Walking and Outdoor Festival	Moray
18-21 June	Church Stretton Walking Festival	Shropshire
26-28 June	Snowdonia Challenge	N Wales
27-28 June	Quantock Walking Festival	Somerset
27June-5 Jul	Otley Walking Festival	W Yorkshire
22-30 Aug	Dartmoor Walking Festival	Devon
4-7 Sept	Much Wenlock Walking Festival	Shropshire
5-6 Sept	Corwen Walking Festival	Denbighshire
5-13 Sept	Bedfordshire Walking Festival	Bedfordshire
7-14 Sept	Scottish Borders Walking Festival	Scottish Border
12-20 Sept	Chesterfield Canal Walking Festival	Derbyshire
12-27 Sept	South Pennines Walk and Ride Festival	Yorks/Lancs
12-27 Sept	Autumn Footprints	Derbyshire
14-20 Sept	Wellington Walking Festival	Shropshire
17-20 Sept	Kington Walking Festival	Herefordshire
19-27 Sept	Richmond Walking and Book Festival	N Yorkshire
19-28 Sept	Barmouth Walking Festival	Gwynedd
2-4 Oct	Ross on Wye Walking Festival	Herefordshire

WALKING FESTIVALS

walksinchepstow.co.uk
kingtonwalks.org
galawalk.co.uk
ulverstonwalkfest.co.uk
ride2stride.co.uk
haltwhistlewalkingfestival.org
ironbridgewalking.co.uk.
llangollenwalkingfestival.co.uk
kendalwalkingfestival.co.uk
bingleywalkersarewelcome.org.uk
trefriwwalkingfestival.co.uk
farnhamwalkingfestival.org
droverstryst.com
gowerwalkingfestival.uk
southdownsway.com
moraywalkoutdoorfest.co.uk
churchstrettonwalkingfestival.co.uk
breeseadventures.co.uk
stoweywalking.co.uk
otleywalkingfestival.co.uk
dartmoorwalkingfestival.co.uk
muchwenlockwalkers.org.uk
corwenwalkingfestival.co.uk
bedswalkfest.co.uk
borderswalking.com
chesterfield-canal-trust.org.uk
pennineprospects.co.uk
autumnfootprints.co.uk
wellingtonwalkersarewelcome.org.uk
kingtonwalks.org
booksandboots.org
barmouthwalkingfestival.co.uk
walkinginross.co.uk

Independent Hostels are working with walking festivals to encourage walking, fresh air and friendship.

Photo: Dartmoor Walking Festival

Independenthostels.co.uk/trails

90 miles	The Pennine Way	Walk
192 miles	Wainwrights Coast to Coast Walk	Walk
200 miles	Mountain Bike Coast to Coast Route	Mountain Bike
140 miles	C2C (Sea to Sea) Cycle Route	Cycle
84 miles	Hadrian's Wall	Walk
80 miles	The Dales Way	Walk
73 miles	Settle to Carlisle Railway	Train
36 miles	Isaac's Tea Trail	Walk
120 miles	Sandstone Way	Mountain Bike
97 miles	St Oswald's Way	Walk
70 miles	Cumbria Way	Walk
24 miles	Yorkshire 3 Peaks	Walk
90 miles	The Dales High Way	Walk
46 miles	The Limestone Way	Walk
60 miles	White Peak Loop	Cycle/Walk
177 miles	Offa's Dyke	Walk
350 miles	Mary Michael Pilgrim's Way	Walk
630 miles	South West Coast Path	Walk
303 miles	Land's End Trail	Walk
850 miles	LEJOG Walk	Walk
874 miles	LEJOG Cycle Route	Cycle
95 miles	Beacons Way	Walk
83 miles	Snowdonia Slate Trail	Walk
291 miles	The Cambrian Way	Walk
861 miles	Wales Coast Path	Walk
250 miles	Lon Las Cymru Cycle Route	Cycle
75 miles	Great Glen Way	Walk
96 miles	West Highland Way	Walk
80 miles	The Rob Roy Way	Walk
537 miles	The Scottish National Trail	Walk
516 miles	Scottish North Coast 500	Road Route
156 miles	Hebridean Way	Walk/Cycle

LONG DISTANCE TRAILS

North England
North England
North England
North England
North England
North England
North England
North Pennines
Northumberland
Northumberland
Cumbria
Yorkshire
Yorkshire
Staffs/Derbys
Derbyshire
Welsh Borders
West Country
South West Eng
Cornwall
UK
UK
South Wales
North Wales
Wales
Wales
Wales
Scotland
Scotland
Scotland
Scotland
North Scotland
Outer Hebridies

Look on the website for the locations of bunkhouses and hostels along iconic long distance routes.

Keep Checking online. New routes are added every month!

Photo: Hadrian's Wall near Slack House Farm pg 211

THE WORLD OF IHUK

Independent Hostels UK is a network of 420+ accommodation owners. We are very different to online travel agents who charge commission or service fees.

Here you will find hostels and bunkhouses across the UK. In the mountains, national parks, city centres and on the coast.

Contact the accommodation direct (using the information in this guide or the network's website) to avoid you or your host paying bookings fees.

Welcome to a world of Independent Hostels

Top Left: Shining Cliff Hostel pg 123a
Bottom Left: Pantyrathro Int Hostel pg 253

Bottom: Ashclyst Farm Hostel pg 65

Left: Clink261 pg 95

Above: Cohort pg 44b

CITY, BACKPACKERS
& BOUTIQUE HOSTELS

City centre hostels and backpacker hostels cater for independent travellers exploring the UK. Close to public transport hubs, they are ideal for young travellers from overseas.

They are also perfect venues for UK groups and individuals attending city events. These hostels are great places to meet people and make new friends, with many offering social events.

Independenthostels.co.uk/city

DOG FRIENDLY

Over 100 hostels and bunkhouses welcome dogs by arrangement.

They are ideal for holidays, weekend breaks or a single night stop-over on a long journey.

Look out for this symbol:-

Independenthostels.co.uk/dog

Top Left: Caerhafod Lodge pg 260

Preseli Ventures Eco Lodge pg 259

FAMILY ROOMS

Large private rooms are ideal for families.

Look out for this symbol [P] which shows private rooms are available, which may be suitable for families.

Or go to our website and look for [F]. The family room symbol.

Great holidays for families of all sizes

PRIVATE ROOMS

Many bunkhouses and hostels have private rooms.

Double, twin, three, four, five, six beds or more. Book a private room the perfect size for your family or group.

Some hostels and bunkhouses have en suite private rooms.

Look out for this symbol

Privacy at night, social in the daytime

Skye Basecamp pg 355

LARGE GROUPS

Hostels and bunkhouses are great for large groups.

Schools, clubs and groups of friends and families return year after year.

With large well equipped kitchens, dining rooms and lounges there is space for everyone.

Groups can book sole use of the whole site.

Independenthostels.co.uk/groups

Top Left: Jersey Accommodation Centre pg 42a
Bottom Left: Exmoor Bunk Barn pg 60   Bottom: Derwentwater Independent Hostel pg 193

OUTDOOR ACTIVITIES

Many hostels and bunkhouses can provide outdoor activities on-site or nearby.

Ideal for schools, clubs, corporate team building. and groups of friends and families.

Try something new

Left: Lockerbrook Farm Outdoor Centre pg 145

Bottom: Smiddy Bunkhouse pg 340

Lowick Old School pg 178

PARTY WEEKENDS

Stag, hen and party weekends are welcomed by some hostels and bunkhouses. Where remote locations make for happy neighbours.

Outdoor activities and catering are often optional extras.

Check the venue is ideal for parties when you make your booking.

Independenthostels.co.uk/parties

CELEBRATIONS

Hostels and bunkhouses make unique venues for celebrations and weddings.

Much cheaper than hotels they offer accommodation and large areas for parties.

Celebrate that big birthday or anniversary surrounded by family and friends.

Why not make a weekend of it and discover a wonderful new area of the UK.

Good value and unique

Bunkhouse at the Workhouse pg 278

FOR ALL AGES

Hostels provide ideal accommodation for people of all ages. Many people who discovered youth hostels in their youth still enjoy walking holidays in rural hostels. City hostels are ideal for young independent travellers.

3G HOLIDAYS

The varied accommodation provided by hostels can be booked sole use for three generation holidays.

There are private rooms for the grandparents and family rooms for parents and young children. Older children and teenagers enjoy the opportunity for a sleepover sharing a larger room.

Catering tasks can be shared, grandparents & grandchildren get to spend time together and cousins devise new games.

The three generations join together, often from different parts of the country to spend quality time together.

Accommodation to suit all ages

Left Top: Wooler Youth Hostel pg 226
Left Bottom: Royal Mile Backpackers pg 314a   Below:Left Dalebridge (old sign), Below Right Mounthooly Bunkh. pg 224

FRESH AIR HOLIDAYS

Most people staying in rural bunkhouses and hostels are enjoying holidays in the fresh air.

You will find hostels in the mountains, on the coast, among the rolling hills and in the national parks.

Hostels and bunkhouses are ideal for families enjoying fresh air breaks and can be booked for sole use by cycling and walking clubs.

Accommodation for oudoor enthusiasts

Top Left: Dale House Barn pg 165
Bottom Left: Mid Wales Bunkhouse pg 268

Bottom: All Stretton Bunkhouse pg 110

Wooler Youth Hostel pg 226

BIKE SHEDS

Many bunkhouses and hostels pride themselves on having cycle sheds and equipment stores.

Look out for this symbol

On our website the extra symbol ⓘ indicates that the store is secure.

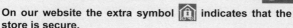

Independenthostels.co.uk/bike-sheds

DRYING ROOMS

Many hostels and bunkhouses have drying facilities.

You can go out in all weathers and be sure of a dry start the next day.

Look out for this symbol

Don't let the weather stop you

Skye Basecamp pg 355

Left: Tower Windmill pg 118   *Above: Bransdale Mill Bunkhouse pg 152*

NATIONAL TRUST
BUNKHOUSES AND BOTHIES

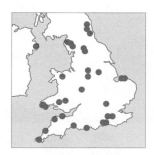

There are over 30 National Trust bunkhouses and bothies in the Independent Hostel Guide.
Located on National Trust estates or along unspoilt coastlines.

The bunkhouses are ideal for groups looking for comfortable self-catering accommodation. The bothies are an escape from modern life, often with simple sleeping platforms, no electricity and cold water.

Independenthostels.co.uk/nt

 = Green Tourism GOLD   = Green Tourism SILVER   = Green Tourism BRONZE

www.green-tourism.com

Left: Palace Farm pg 87

Above: Chartners Farm pg 220

ECO HOSTELS
AND BUNKHOUSES

Hostels and bunkhouses have a naturally low CO_2 footprint. Shared accommodation means shared resources, making your holidays more sustainable.

This map shows hostels and bunkhouses which, in addition to their natural eco advantages, have sustainability at the heart of their business.

Those that have achieved Green Tourism awards will also have the symbols shown opposite on their features.

Independenthostels.co.uk/eco

Skiddaw House Hostel pg 192a

YHA PAST & PRESENT

Many of the hostels sold by the YHA are now being run as independent hostels.

Over 60 former YHA properties are featured in this guide.

Those still affilliated to the YHA have this symbol

Independenthostels.co.uk/yha

CAMPING BARNS & BOTHIES

Camping barns offer simple accommodation in remote locations.

In essence a stone tent, you will need to bring your own bedding and often cooking equipment too.

They are great for back-to-basics escapes.

All camping barns and bothies feature 🏠 (the simple symbol) on their page. As will the most basic of bunkhouses.

independenthostels.co.uk/barns

The Reckoning House pg 132

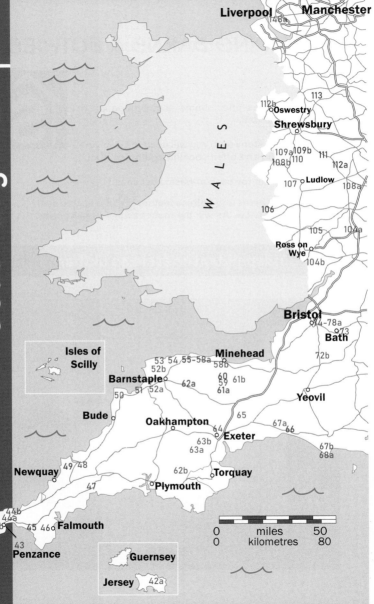

Liverpool
Manchester
148a

113

112b
Oswestry
Shrewsbury

109a 109b
108a 110   111   112a
107 Ludlow   108a

106

105   104a

Ross on
Wye   104b

Bristol
74-78a
73
Bath

72b

Isles of
Scilly

Minehead
53 54 55-58a
52b   58b
Barnstaple   62a   60   61b
59
50   51 52a   61a
Yeovil

Bude   65
Oakhampton   64   67a 66
63b   Exeter
63a   67b
68a
Newquay   49 48
62b   Torquay
47   Plymouth

44b
44a
42b
45 46   Falmouth
43
Penzance   Guernsey

Jersey   42a

WALES

0   miles   50
0   kilometres   80

South England

KEY

45 - **Page number**

45a - **Left side of page**

45b - **Right side of page**

45 - **Groups only**

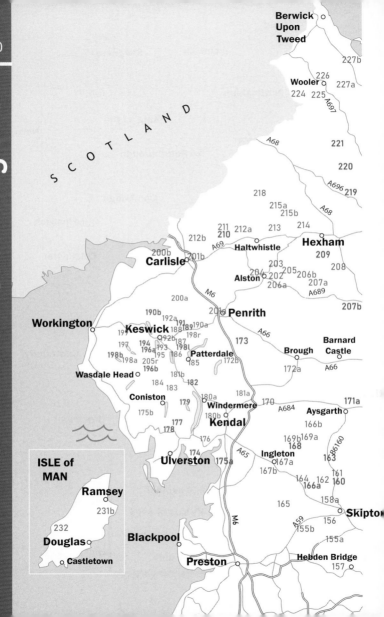

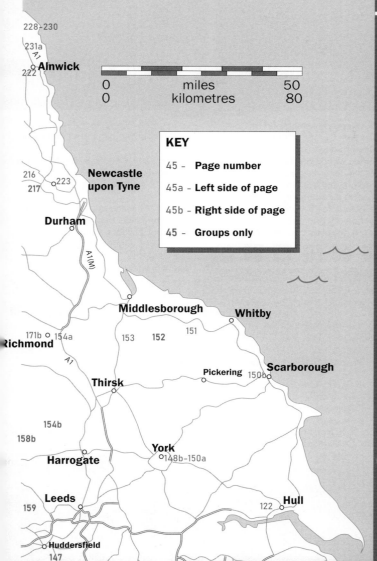

228-230
231a
A1
222 o **Alnwick**

0   miles   50
0   kilometres   80

KEY

45 -   **Page number**
45a - **Left side of page**
45b - **Right side of page**
45 -   **Groups only**

216
217   o 223   **Newcastle upon Tyne**

Durham

A1(M)

o   **Middlesborough**   **Whitby** o

153   152   151

171b o 154a
Richmond   A1   153   152

Pickering   150b   **Scarborough**

Thirsk o

154b
158b

York o 148b-150a

Harrogate o

Leeds o
159   122 o **Hull**

o **Huddersfield**
147

North England

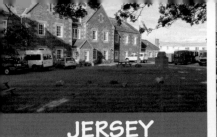

JERSEY
ACCOMMODATION CENTRE
42a

Close to the pretty fishing port of Gorey in St. Martins. Camping and a range of B&B rooms from twin en suites to private dormitories with shared showers. The perfect mix for individuals or groups. Large communal WiFi lounge with TV & DVDs and a games room. Additional costs include: self catering kitchen, sauna, laundry and packed lunches. Adventure activities can be arranged.

DETAILS
■ **Open** - March-Oct. Reception 8:30 - 4pm or 8pm depending on the season
■ **Beds** 113: Bunks: 1x10,6x8,1x6,4x4. En suite: 1x8, 1x4, 1x5, 2x3, 4x2, 2x1.
■ **Price/night** - B&B: £30.75-£32.75pp. B&B en suites: £32.75-£34.75pp. Twin £32.75-£34.75pp. Youth groups £28pp.

CONTACT: Anna Stammers
Tel: 01534 498636
info@jerseyhostel.co.uk
www.jerseyhostel.co.uk
La Rue de la Pouclee et des Quatre Chemins, St Martins, Jersey, JE3 6DU

LANDS END
HOSTEL
42b

Land's End Hostel, in the hamlet of Trevescan, is 1/2 mile from Land's End.

Double glazed & centrally heated it has a fully equipped kitchen & dining areas inside & out.

Modern bathrooms and bedrooms with TVs & WiFi. New bunk beds with USB ports & LED lights. Bedding / towels supplied.

Bike storage, parking & small shop.

DETAILS
■ **Open** - All year.
■ **Beds** - 14: 2×2, 1×4, 1×6 ensuite
■ **Price/night** - From £25pp (continental breakfast £5.50).

CONTACT: Lou
Tel: 07585 625774
lou@landsendholidays.co.uk
www.landsendholidays.co.uk
Mill Barn, Trevescan, Sennan, Nr Land's End, Penzance, TR19 7AQ

PENZANCE
BACKPACKERS

43

Whether you're looking for sandy beaches and sheltered coves, the storm lashed cliffs of Land's End, sub-tropical gardens, international artists, the remains of ancient cultures, or just somewhere to relax and take time out,
Penzance Backpackers is for you. Situated close to the sea front and the town centre, accommodation is mostly in small bunk-bedded rooms. Linen is provided. Lots of local information and a warm welcome all included.

DETAILS
- **Open** - Mar-Oct.10am-Noon, 5-10pm.
- **Beds** - 30: 2 double, 1x4 (double + 2 bunks), 3x6, 1x7.
- **Price/night** - From £18.50 per person. £42 for 2 people in private room.

CONTACT: Mathew
Tel: 01736 363836
info@pzbackpack.com
www.pzbackpack.com
The Blue Dolphin, Alexandra Road,
Penzance, TR18 4LZ

LOWER PENDERLEATH
FARM HOSTEL
44a

COHORT
44b
HOSTEL

Just three miles from St Ives' beaches & 5 miles from Penzance, Lower Penderleath Farm Hostel provides self-catering accommodation in four twin rooms and one alpine dormitory for 12. Plus a self contained family maisonette with small kitchen and private shower & toilet. BYO sleeping bags. Pub food in two local villages is within walking distance. Bedding not provided.

Located in the centre of St Ives, Cohort is sytlish and comfortable. Great facilities include a hot shower in the courtyard for surfers, through to a laundry & dry room. The on-site bar is cheap; there's a big guest kitchen; free super fast WiFi; a TV room & comfortable pod beds - all with USB ports, lights, curtains & under-bed storage. Free tea & coffee before 10am. Walk outside to find cafés, bars, galleries, Tate St Ives and four spectacular beaches. The SW Coast Path is 5 minutes from the front door.

DETAILS

- **Open** - Easter-Oct. Arrive between 9am-6pm, depart by 10am.
- **Beds** - 24: 4x2 + dorm platform of 12, 1x4 self contained maisonette
- **Price/night** - £18pp, £38 twin room. £100 maisonette. Minimum of 2 nights. Sorry no cards. Cash payment only.

CONTACT: Russell Rogers
Tel: 07723 014567
rusrogers60@gmail.com
www.stivescampingandhostel.com
Lower Penderleath Farm, Towednack,
St.Ives, Cornwall, TR26 3AF

DETAILS

- **Open** - Feb-Dec. Reception 8am-11pm.
- **Beds** - 61: 1x8, 7x6, 1x4, 2x twin, 1x twin/double/triple
- **Price/night** - From £17

CONTACT: Reception
Tel: 01736 791664
hello@stayatcohort.co.uk
www.stayatcohort.co.uk
The Stennack, St Ives,
Cornwall, TR26 1FF

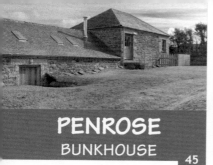

PENROSE
BUNKHOUSE
45

On the edge of the Penrose Estate, the gateway to The Lizard Peninsula. Penrose bunkhouse is right next to the SW Coast Path and has great access to many local walks, trails and cycling routes. Penrose, is home to many rare species of wildlife as well as Cornwall's largest freshwater lake, the Loe.

A perfect location to base your group for wildlife adventures, walking and activity holidays or a break away from it all. The bunkhouse sleeps 16 in three rooms and is well equipped for self-catering.

      GROUPS ONLY

DETAILS
- **Open** - All year. All day
- **Beds** - 16: 2x7, 1x2,
- **Price/night** - From £350 for two nights.

CONTACT: National Trust Holidays
Tel: 03443 351296
bunkhouses@nationaltrust.org.uk
www.nationaltrust.org.uk/holidays
Penrose Bunk House, Gunwalloe,
Helston, Cornwall TR12 7PY

FALMOUTH
LODGE BACKPACKERS
46

Relaxed, friendly and clean, Falmouth Lodge Backpackers is just two minutes' walk from the Blue Flag Gyllyngvase beach and the South West Coast Path. Only eight minutes' walk into town with its exotic gardens, art galleries, Maritime Museum, Pendennis Castle, and the harbour. Free parking and WiFi. Complimentary tea, coffee and breakfast. Well-equipped kitchen and cosy lounge.

DETAILS

■ **Open** - Open Feb-Oct. Sole use Nov/Dec/Jan. Reception open from 5pm
■ **Beds** - 28: 2x2/3, 2x4/5, 1x6/7, 1xdbl/family en suite (some sea views).
■ **Price/night** - From £19 pp. Sole use £616, with discounts in Nov/Dec/Jan. Discounts for multiple nights.

CONTACT: Judi
Tel: 01326 319996 or 07525 722808
judi@falmouthlodge.co.uk
www.falmouthbackpackers.co.uk
9 Gyllyngvase Terrace, Falmouth,
Cornwall, TR11 4DL

EDENS YARD
BACKPACKERS

Welcome to this quirky, camino inspired eco hostel up-cycled from an old stable block to include mixed bunk rooms, a courtyard kitchen & a communal lounge.

It's just a short leafy lane from the Eden Project situated on National Cycle Routes 2 & 3, two miles from the Northwest Coast Path at Carlyon Bay and close to the historic Saints Way pilgrimage trail. Walkers and cyclists are welcomed and pick-ups from the station or parking can be arranged.

DETAILS

- **Open** - Easter to mid Sept. Arrive between 4 & 10pm please.
- **Beds** - 1x6, 1x8
- **Price/night** - £15

CONTACT: Neal or Julia
Tel: 01726 814907
info@edensyard.uk
www.edensyard.uk
17 Tregrehan Mills, St. Austell, Cornwall, PL25 3TL

MANOR HOUSE
ACTIVITY CENTRE
48

Manor House Activity Centre offers top quality accommodation for couples, families & groups of all sizes just 3 miles from Padstow & the north Cornish coast.

Sleeping up to 58 across 9 rooms the spacious Georgian manor house oozes style & has a private garden with BBQ area & hot tub. Catering & outdoor activities are also available.

Great walking & cycling on the doorstep. BYO bedding or hire.

DETAILS

- **Open** - All year
- **Beds** - 58: 2x12, 1x10, 1x8, 1x6, 1x4, 3x2
- **Price/night** - From £25 pp. Min stay 2 nights. Discounts for large groups.

CONTACT: Lesley Kirk
Tel: 01841 540346
enquiries@manoractivitycentre.co.uk
www.manoractivitycentre.co.ukSt Issey, Wadebridge, Cornwall, PL27 7QB

BEACH HEAD
BUNKHOUSE

With fantastic views out to sea and along the north Cornish coast to Trevose Head, the National Trust run Beach Head Bunkhouse provides great value basic self-catering holiday accommodation.

The centrally heated, self-catering facilities and great location just 1.5 miles from the beach at Porthcothan and close to the South West Coast path make it the perfect base for family holidays and walking groups alike. A large, woodburning stove provides a cosy feel. Not suitable for very young children.

        GROUPS ONLY

DETAILS

- **Open** - All year. All day
- **Beds** - 14: 2x1 2x6
- **Price/night** - 2 nights from £380

CONTACT: National Trust Holidays
Tel: 03443 351296
bunkhouses@nationaltrust.org.uk
www.nationaltrust.org.uk/holidays
Park Head, St Eval, Wadebridge,
Cornwall, PL27 7UU

ELMSCOTT
HOSTEL
50

Elmscott Hostel is surrounded by unspoiled coastline with sea views of Lundy Island. Great for walking, cycling, surfing and bird watching. The South West Coast Path is just a few mins' walk away. The hostel is well equipped for all your self-catering needs and has a games room and shop. In winter it is only available for sole use bookings.

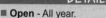

DETAILS

- **Open** - All year.
- **Beds** - 32 (35 in winter): 1 unit of 20: 2x6, 2x4; 1 unit of 12: 1x6, 1x4, 1x2. Extra 3 bed room for sole use in winter.
- **Price/night** - Adult £23-£25, under 16s £16-£18. Discounts for groups or longer stays.

CONTACT: John, Thirza and Kate
Tel: Hostel 01237 441367/ Owners
01237 441276/ Kate 01237 441637
john.goa@virgin.net
www.elmscott.org.uk
Elmscott, Hartland, Bideford, Devon,
EX39 6ES

PEPPERCOMBE
BOTHY

Located in a quiet, tranquil, wooded valley with views across Bideford Bay towards Lundy, Peppercombe Bothy is effectively a stone tent.

A perfect stopover on the South West Coast Path which passes through the valley or for those who really do want to get away from it all. With access to it's own secluded beach you will not be disappointed. There is no light or heating so bring your own sleeping, cooking and eating equipment and a torch!

DETAILS
- **Open** - All year. All day
- **Beds** - 4: BYO mats & sleeping bags
- **Price/night** - From £22 for whole bothy.

CONTACT: National Trust Holidays
Tel: 03443 351296
bunkhouses@nationaltrust.org.uk
www.nationaltrust.org.uk/holidays
Peppercombe, Bideford,
Devon, EX39 5QD

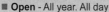

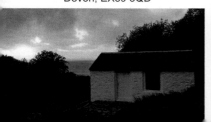

SEALOCK BARN

52a

MULLACOTT
CAMPING BARN

52b

OPENING SPRING 2020. This converted workshop on a restored section of the heritage Rolle canal in rural Devon sleeps up to 10 in 3 rooms. Surrounded by a county wildlife site & salt marshes there is abundant wildlife. Facilities include an open plan kitchen/living/dining area and two WC/shower rooms. The barn has direct access to the Tarka Trail, perfect for walking or cycling. Guests will also enjoy direct access to the tidal River Torridge for canoeing & fishing. BYO sleeping bags.

Set in 30 acres on the North Devon coast, the farm boasts sea views overlooking Woolacombe, Lundy Island, Lee Bay, Ilfracombe, and the Welsh coast. A former stable block with all accommodation on ground level with raised sleeping areas with mattresses. BYO sleeping bag/bedding and warm clothing. There is a dining area and well equipped kitchen. Toilets/coin operated showers are in a nearby block. No stag/hen parties. Dogs welcome with sole use bookings. B&B, camping and a static caravan are also available on site.

DETAILS
- **Open** - All year.
- **Beds** - 10: 1x4, 2x3 + camping
- **Price/night** - £10pp midweek, £12 pp weekend. Enquire for whole barn

DETAILS
- **Open** - March - November
- **Beds** - 20
- **Price/night** - £10 per person. Sole use: by arrangement.

CONTACT: Hilary Wills
Tel: 01237 477705
hilarywills@yahoo.co.uk

Vale Cottage, 7 Annery Kiln, Weare Giffard, Bideford, EX39 5JE

CONTACT: Alison and Adrian Homa
Tel: 01271 866877
relax@mullacottfarm.co.uk
www.mullacottfarm.co.uk
Ilfracombe, Devon, EX34 8NA

OCEAN
BACKPACKERS

Close to the picturesque Ilfracombe Harbour, this clean and friendly hostel offers fantastic facilities for walkers, cyclists, surfers, families, schools and activity groups. Providing self-catering accommodation with great facilities including, communal lounge (free WiFi), bike/surfboard storage, drying area and free parking. Ilfracombe is full of cafés, galleries, shops and restaurants and is home to Damien Hirst's statue, Verity.

DETAILS

- **Open** - March-Nov. Reception 9-12 noon and 4pm-10pm. No curfew.
- **Beds** - 54:- 1x8, 5x6, 1 x single, 2 x double, 3 x double & bunk
- **Price/night** - Dorm beds £13-£20pp. Double/twin rooms £45-£50 per room.

CONTACT: Chris and Abby
Tel: 01271 867835 or 07866 667716
info@oceanbackpackers.co.uk
www.oceanbackpackers.co.uk
29 St James Place, Ilfracombe, Devon,
EX34 9BJ

HEDDON ORCHARD
BOTHY
54

Heddon Orchard Bothy is a four person hideaway located deep in the remote Heddon Valley. Close to the South West Coast Path and Heddon's Mouth pebble beach on the Exmoor coast.

Embrace this remote rustic accommodation by bringing your own bedding/mats, cooking/BBQ equipment and a torch for the starlit walk to the toilet/washroom. The welcoming Hunter's Inn Hotel is just 50 metres away.

DETAILS
- **Open** - All year, arive after 3.30pm leave before 10am.
- **Beds** - 4: 1x4 (sleeping platform)
- **Price/night** - From £21 to £28 (depending on season).

CONTACT: National Trust Holidays
Tel: 0344 335 1296
bunkhouses@nationaltrust.org.uk
www.nationaltrust.org.uk/holidays
Heddon Valley, Jose's Ln, Barnstaple
EX31 4PY

BUTTER HILL
BARN

This cosy National Trust bunkhouse with woodburning stove & electric radiators, sits on the A39 at Countisbury, close to Lynton & Lynmouth on the North Devon Coast. Surrounded by the dramatic Watersmeet Valleys & Exmoor, it is close to the South West Coastal Path & Atlantic surf beaches. Perfect for families, groups & walkers, the barn is just along the road from Exmoor Bunkhouse (see page 56), so it can be used as an overspill for larger groups. The Blue Ball, an old coaching inn, is opposite.

DETAILS

- **Open** - All year.
- **Beds** - 6: 1x6
- **Price/night** - 2 nights from £120.

CONTACT: National Trust Holidays
Tel: 0344 335 1296
bunkhouses@nationaltrust.org.uk
www.nationaltrust.org.uk/holidays
Countisbury Hill, Lynmouth, Devon,
EX35 6NE

EXMOOR

BUNKHOUSE

56

Owned and managed by the National Trust, Exmoor Bunkhouse is the perfect base for groups or families visiting Exmoor National Park.

Located at Countisbury, the bunkhouse is close to the Watersmeet Valleys and the picturesque North Devon coastal villages of Lynton and Lynmouth.

Enjoy walking, horse riding or surfing on nearby Atlantic coast beaches. Larger groups can holiday together at nearby Butter Hill Barn, (see page 55).

GROUPS ONLY

DETAILS

- **Open** - All year. 24 hours.
- **Beds** - 18: 2x8, 1x2
- **Price/night** - 2 nights' minimum stay from £270 mid week and £390 weekend.

CONTACT: National Trust Holidays
Tel: 03443 351296
bunkhouses@nationaltrust.org.uk
www.nationaltrust.org.uk/holidays
Countisbury, Lynton, Devon, EX35 6NE

FORELAND
BOTHY

Foreland Bothy on the National Trust Foreland Point Estate on the Exmoor coast offers very basic accommodation, but rewards you with a fantastic location right on the South West Coast Path.

Treat it like camping but without the tent, so you need to bring camping mats, sleeping bags and cooking equipment. There is a composting loo but no hot water. The perfect location for a night or two for those who want to escape technology in this wilderness under some stunning dark skies.

DETAILS
- **Open** - All year. All day
- **Beds** - 4: 1x4 platforms
- **Price/night** - From £23 sole use.

CONTACT: National Trust Holidays
Tel: 03443 351296
bunkhouses@nationaltrust.org.uk
www.nationaltrust.org.uk/holidays
Lighthouse Road, Countisbury, Lynton,
Devon, EX35 6NE

BERRY LAWN
LINHAY BOTHY
58a

58b

BASE LODGE

Berry Lawn Linhay Bothy is a stone tent perched on top of some of England's highest cliffs, with amazing views over the Bristol Channel, Watersmeet Valley and Exmoor.

Ideal as an overnight stop for walkers on the South West Coast Path the bothy welcomes up to two dogs and has no parking.

There is a pub in 500m and the seaside town of Lynmouth is 2 miles away.

Base Lodge is your perfect base for exploring Exmoor, the Quantocks and North Devon. The South West Coast Path starts in Minehead and there is excellent mountain biking. Guided biking, navigational training, climbing, surfing, pony trekking and natural history walks can all be arranged. Base Lodge is clean, comfortable with self-catering and a cosy log burner.

DETAILS
- **Open** - All year. All day access once booked (reception open from 3pm).
- **Beds** - 22: 2x2, 1x7, 1x6, 1x5
- **Price/night** - Dorms £17.50 (£20 one night), private single £7.50 supplement, twin/double £40. Sole use of Base Lodge from £200. Family room discount.

DETAILS
- **Open** - April to December
- **Beds** - 4: 1x4
- **Price/night** - From £23 to £28 per night for sole use of the bothy.

CONTACT: National Trust Holidays
Tel: 0344 335 1296
bunkhouses@nationaltrust.org.uk
www.nationaltrust.org.uk/holidays
Countisbury Hill, Nr Lymouth, Devon

CONTACT: Wendy or Graham
Tel: 01643 703520 or 07731 651536
togooutdoors@hotmail.com
www.togooutdoors.co.uk
16 The Parks, Minehead, Somerset,
TA24 8BS

EXMOOR
CAMPING BARN

59

Situated on a small farm in the heart of Exmoor National Park, Exmoor Camping Barn offers quality accommodation for 12 and can be booked as a whole or by the room. The Coleridge Way runs through the farm leading to miles of footpaths & bridleways. The nearest beach is 7 miles & the local pub is 3/4 mile away.

DETAILS

■ **Open** - All year. Check in 4-8pm. Check out by 10am

■ **Beds** - 12: 1x2 dbl/twin, 1x4 bunks/2 sgls, 1x6 bunks/2 sgls

■ **Price/night** - Whole barn: from £300. Rooms: 2 bed from £50, 4 bed from £100, 6 bed from £120. Sole use only at peak time, ask for details.

CONTACT: Trish Foxwell
Tel: 01643 841393
enquiries@exmoorcampingbarn.co.uk
exmoorcampingbarn.co.uk
Exmoor Camping Barn, Drapers Way, Wheddon Cross, Minehead, Somerset TA24 7ED

EXMOOR
BUNKBARN

60

Formerly a granary on a working farm, this eco-friendly bunkbarn is close to Winsford Hill and Wimbleball lake. Perfect for exploring Exmoor on foot, bike or canoe. Hot water, central heating & WiFi included in price. Well equipped, open-plan kitchen/dinning with seating for all. Large drying room. Outside BBQ area and small field with campfire. BYO bedding & towels. Sleeps max 25 - sole use only. Free logs for the stove and camp fire. Enjoy Exmoor's dark skies.

DETAILS
- **Open** - All year. All day.
- **Beds** - 25: 1x14, 1x8, 1x3
- **Price/night** - Whole barn only:- Weekend (2 nights minimum) £350 per night. Weekdays £300 per night.

CONTACT: Julia or Guy Everard
Tel: 01643 851410 or 07967 114331
bookings@exmoorbunkbarn.co.uk
www.exmoorbunkbarn.co.uk
Week Farm, Bridgetown, Dulverton
TA22 9JP

NORTHCOMBE
CAMPING BARNS
61a

A mile outside the town of Dulverton on Exmoor, Northcombe Camping Barns nestle in the Barle river valley with good canoeing, walking and bridleways. A perfect base for groups on Exmoor. The barns sleep 16 and 28 in partitioned dormitories. Smaller groups can be catered for. Heated by wood-burning stoves with a well equipped kitchen, you just need to bring your own pillows, sleeping bags or duvets.

     GROUPS ONLY

DETAILS
■ **Open** - All year. Arrive after 4pm, depart before 10.30am
■ **Beds** - 44: Barn16: 1x6, 1x10. Barn28: 1x6, 1x10, 1x12
■ **Price/night** - Sole use: Barn16 from £160, Barn28 from £260. Showers 20p. Electric meter £1 coins.

CONTACT: Sally Harvey
Tel: 01398 323602
sallyeharvey17@gmail.com
www.northcombecampingbarns.co.uk
Hollam, Dulverton, Somerset, TA22 9JH

CHITCOMBE FARM
CAMPING BARNS
61b

A small family farm in West Somerset on the edge of Exmoor, Chitcombe Farm provides inexpensive, basic, warm & dry accommodation. Perfect after a day hiking on Exmoor, or event training.

The Hay Barn, is a dormitory style open plan barn whilst The Cart Shed is an open plan chalet. Both have well equipped kitchens, bathroom with showers, seating areas and central heating. BYO pillows and sleeping bag.

DETAILS
■ **Open** - All year.
■ **Beds** - 16: The Hay Barn 14, The Cart Shed 4. More by arrangement
■ **Price/night** - £20pp. Sole use: The Hay barn £200. The Cart Shed £75.

CONTACT: Ali Kennen
Tel: 01398 371274
stkennen@hotmail.co.uk
chitcombebarns.co.uk
Chitcombe Farm, Huish Champflower, Taunton, Somerset, TA4 2EL

ROCK AND RAPID
BUNKHOUSE
62a

Perfect for an adventurous or relaxing break. The Rock and Rapid Adventure Centre offers activities such as climbing (climbing wall on site for lessons or use by experienced climbers) coasteering, raft building and canoeing. The bunkhouse can be rented out for sole use, or an activity package can be put together for your group. This can vary from a few activities to a full programme, including food.

Just 20 mins from the North Devon coastline. Hen and stags welcome as are family and school groups.

DETAILS
- **Open** - All year. 24 hours.
- **Beds** - 40: 2x18, 2x2
- **Price/night** - £250 per night sole use.

CONTACT: Gareth Chalker
Tel: 01769 309003
info@rockandrapidadventures.co.uk
www.rockandrapidadventures.co.uk
Hacche Mill, South Molton, EX36 3NA

62b
HARFORD
BUNKHOUSE

Harford Bunkhouse & Camping offers comfortable budget accommodation on the edge of stunning South Dartmoor. An ideal choice if you are planning to start the Two Moors Way walk from south to north. Run alongside a working farm, the bunkhouse offers dormitory style accommodation with self catering facilities for up to 50. The campsite is on two of the farm's meadows. There are also two camping pods and a cabin which sleep up to 6 people each.

DETAILS
- **Open** - All year. All day.
- **Beds** - 30: 1x16, 1x6, 2x4 plus pods and camping
- **Price/night** - From £17pp. Camping £8.50pp

CONTACT: Julie Cole
Tel: 07968 566218
julie.cole6@btinternet.com
www.harfordbunkhouse.com
West Combeshead, Harford, Ivybridge, Devon, PL21 0JG

SPARROWHAWK
BACKPACKERS
63a

BLYTHESWOOD
HOSTEL
63b

A small, friendly eco-hostel in the centre of Moretonhampstead, Dartmoor National Park. Popular with cyclists, hikers, bikers, wild swimmers, artists and photographers, A beautifully converted stone stable, with solar-heated showers, kitchen, courtyard, BBQ and secure bike shed. High open moorland, rocky tors, ancient burial sites, stone circles, woods and clear rivers close by. Moretonhampstead has shops, cafés, art galleries and pubs. Cicerone LEJOG & Dartmoor Way cycle routes pass by.

In secluded, native woodland on the eastern edge of Dartmoor, the cabin has been a hostel since the 1930s. Friendly and peaceful, with a homely living room, wood burner, self-catering kitchen, picnic tables, BBQ and fire pit. Walk straight from the door to Heltor and Blackingstone Rock or along the river to Fingle Bridge and Castle Drogo. Cross stepping stones to Dunsford village. Near Moretonhampstead and Exeter. On the LEJOG cycling route.

DETAILS

- **Open** - All year
- **Beds** - 18: 1x14 + double/family room.
- **Price/night** - Adults dorm £19. U14 £10. Double room £45 (for 2 people).

DETAILS

- **Open** - All year.
- **Beds** - 16: 1x6, 1x4 (family), 1x2 (cabin) and 1x4 (family cabin)
- **Price/night** - £18 per adult. U16 £12. Sole use: £275pn.

CONTACT: Alison
Tel: 01647 440318 or 07870 513570
ali@sparrowhawkbackpackers.co.uk
www.sparrowhawkbackpackers.co.uk
45 Ford Street, Moretonhampstead, Dartmoor, Devon, TQ13 8LN

CONTACT: Lewis or Sarah
Tel: 07758 654840
hello@blytheswood.co.uk
www.blytheswood.co.uk
Steps Bridge, Dunsford, Devon
EX6 7EQ

EXETER GLOBE
BACKPACKERS

64

Globe Backpackers offers clean, comfortable, self catering accommodation.
It is just a few minutes' walk from Exeter's city centre with its cathedral, picturesque historic waterway, quay and wide range of shops, pubs, clubs, cafés and restaurants.

DETAILS

■ **Open** - All year (phone for Xmas). Check in/check out: Mon-Fri: 8.30-12.00 & 3.30-11pm. Sat,Sun: 8.30am-11pm. Earlier check out by arrangement only.,
■ **Beds** - 46-52: 1x10, 3x8, 1x6, 3x2/4 (dbl/twin plus bunk bed)
■ **Price/night** - Dorms from £17.50pp or £80pp per week. Private rooms from £50 for two people, £80 for four people. £5 key deposit.

CONTACT: Duty Manager
Tel: 01392 215521
info@exeterbackpackers.co.uk
www.exeterbackpackers.co.uk
71 Holloway Street, Exeter, EX2 4JD

ASHCLYST FARM
HOSTEL
65

Ashclyst Farm Hostel is a charming National Trust farm house on an organic arable farm at the edge of Ashclyst Forest. There are double, twin, and triple rooms. The beds are fully made up with duvets and the bedrooms are spacious and quiet.

Guests have full use of the farmhouse kitchen, dining rooms and lounge, and camping is available for larger groups.

DETAILS

- **Open** - Spring, Summer, Autumn.
- **Beds** - 11: 2 x twin, 2 x dbl, 1 x triple plus camping for larger groups
- **Price/night** - £23pp. Twin/double rooms £46. Entire house £250 + £10 per camper.

CONTACT: Lorraine or Martyn.
Tel: 01392 461302
lorraineglover@hotmail.co.uk
ashclystfarmhostel.com
Harepathstead Rd, Broadclyst, East Devon, EX5 3DF

STONE BARROW
BUNKHOUSE

66

On the National Trust Golden Cap Estate, this bunkhouse has been converted from an old MoD radar station and provides fantastic group accommodation for families, walkers or special interest groups.

With great views over Golden Cap, Lyme Bay and Chesil Beach it is the perfect base for a walking or beach holiday with Charmouth beaches only half an hour walk away. Stone Barrow Bunkhouse sleeps 8 in two 4 bed dorms and is well equipped for group self-catering.

         GROUPS ONLY

DETAILS

- **Open** - All year. All day
- **Beds** - 8: 2x4
- **Price/night** - From £160 for two nights.

CONTACT: National Trust Holidays
Tel: 03443 351296
bunkhouses@nationaltrust.org.uk
www.nationaltrust.org.uk/holidays
Stonebarrow Lane, Charmouth, Dorset,
DT6 6RA

MONKTON WYLD
COURT
67a

This Victorian neo-Gothic mansion in Dorset's AONB has easy access to the Jurassic Coast at Lyme Regis as well as the Wessex and Monarch's Way long distance footpaths. Guests can use the vegetarian self-catering kitchen to prepare their own meals or vegetarian meals can be pre-booked. There is also camping in the grounds. Run by a charity that promotes sustainable living. Fruit and vegetables are grown in the organic garden and Jersey cows provide the dairy products.

DETAILS
■ **Open** - All year. Office opening hours: 9am-5pm.
■ **Beds** - 42 beds in various room sizes.
■ **Price/night** - £20 - £37.50pp

CONTACT: Office Team
Tel: 01297 560342
info@monktonwyldcourt.org
www.monktonwyldcourt.co.uk
Elsdon's Lane, Monkton Wyld, Nr Charmouth, Dorset, DT6 6DQ

BHP BUDGET
ACCOMMODATION
67b

In the heart of Weymouth, the gateway to the Jurassic coast. With a mixture of bunk rooms with the plus of double en suite rooms. Close to the town centre, the safe swimming waters of the beach & the old harbour which hosts fantastic festivals of the sea. Go wind and kite surfing, fishing, sailing, diving or rock climbing. Sole use possible for groups of up to 23. Facilities include large self-catering kitchen, lounge with Freeview TV & DVD. No stag/hen or party groups.

DETAILS
■ **Open** - All year. Arrivals 2 pm onwards.
■ **Beds** - 23: 3x4, 1x3, 2x2, 2x double en suites
■ **Price/night** - Dorms from £18.50. Private rooms from £32. Sole use of building from £216 (sleeps 23).

CONTACT: BhP Budget Accommodation
Tel: 01305 789257
bunkhouseplus@gmail.com
www.bunkhouseplus.co.uk
47 Walpole Street, Weymouth, DT4 7HQ

THE BUNKER
PORTLAND
68a

MYTIME
OUTDOOR CENTRE
68b

The Bunker is on the South West Coastal Path, with Chesil Beach on its doorstep and world class sport climbing, diving sites and water-sports a short distance away. Sleeping up to 18 in 6 private bunk rooms, each with a shower and sink, The Bunker offers bunk & breakfast and self-catering accommodation for groups and individuals. It has a large communal area, kitchen with tea and coffee making facilities and free WiFi. Packed lunches and evening meals available on request.

Located on the Isle of Purbeck, just outside the picturesque village of Worth Matravers, the rustic MyTime Outdoor Centre provides ideal accommodation for groups wishing to explore the magnificent Jurassic coastline.

Experience the enviable range of outdoor activities nearby; from walking and cycling to coasteering and kayaking. Groups have sole use of the centre.

DETAILS
- **Open** - All year. Check in from 15:00, check out by 10:00
- **Beds** - 18: 3x4,3x2, private bunkrooms
- **Price/night** - Ranging from £15 to £27 per person. Exclusive hire available.

DETAILS
- **Open** - All year.
- **Beds** - 40: 24 inside: 1x2, 1x4 en suite, 1x8, 1x10. 16 camping.
- **Price/night** - Whole centre from £350 (24 people). 16 more can camp (BYO tents) at £7pppn. Bedding £5pp. Dog £10.

CONTACT: Tony or Sally
Tel: 07846 401010
stay@thebunkerportland.com
www.thebunkerportland.com
The Bunker, Victoria Square, Portland, Dorset, DT5 1AL

CONTACT: MyTime Outdoor Centre
Tel: 07920 102323
bookings@mytimecharity.co.uk
www.mytimecharity.co.uk
Off Renscombe Rd, Worth Matravers, Isle of Purbeck, Dorset. BH19 3LL

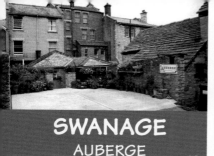

SWANAGE
AUBERGE

Family run, Swanage Auberge is a refuge for climbers, cyclists, walkers & divers at the eastern end of the Jurassic Coast. In the centre of Swanage, a stone's throw from the South West Coast Path, there is excellent walking, mountain biking, diving and rock climbing close by. There is a fully equipped self-catering kitchen and a packed lunch service if required. Parking for 2 vehicles is available on a first come first served basis & free on-street parking is close by.

DETAILS

- **Open** - All year (phone mobile if no reply). All day.
- **Beds** - 15: 1x6, 1x4, 1x5
- **Price/night** - £20pp, £18 for 2+ nights. Inc bedding/towel, cereal breakfast, tea & coffee. Group rates. No credit cards.

CONTACT: Pete or Pam
Tel: 01929 424368 or 07711 117668
bookings@swanageauberge.co.uk
www.swanageauberge.co.uk
45 High St, Swanage, Dorset, BH19 2LX

SOUTH SHORE
LODGE

70

South Shore Lodge is on the south coast of Brownsea Island in Poole Harbour. It is a Victorian lodge, available to hire year-round by youth, community, special interest, corporate and school groups. There is also some availability for hire by groups of families and friends. With its own garden, beach access, shower block and views of the Purbeck Hills, the lodge sleeps 24 in 5 rooms and is well equipped for self-catering. Access to Brownsea Island is by foot on a ferry from Sandbanks/Poole.

        GROUPS ONLY

DETAILS
- **Open** - All year. All day
- **Beds** - 24: 3x6, 1x4, 1x2
- **Price/night** - £380 per night with a 2 night minimum stay.

CONTACT: National Trust Holidays
Tel: 0344 335 1296
bunkhouses@nationaltrust.org.uk
www.nationaltrust.org.uk/holidays
Brownsea Island, Poole,
Dorset, BH13 7EE

SOUTHSEA ROCKS
HOTEL
71

Southsea Rocks Hotel has a variety of rooms from great value hotel rooms with en suite options to cool hostel dorms.

There are social areas, an outdoor courtyard to sit in the sun and space for guests to enjoy take outs from local restaurants. It is within walking distance of the castle, common and aquarium and is a great base for exploring other attractions including Portsmouth's historic dockyard, Charles Dickens' birthplace and The Mary Rose Museum.

DETAILS
- **Open** - All year. All day
- **Beds** - 28: 2x2, 3x3, 1x4, 1x5, 1x9
- **Price/night** - Private rooms from £40, beds in dorm also available.

CONTACT: Reception
Tel: 02392 820110 or 07510 800761
info@southsearockshotel.co.uk
www.southsearockshotel.co.uk
4 Florence Rd, Portsmouth,
Southsea PO5 2NE

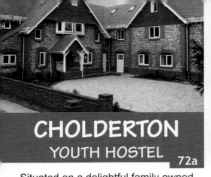

CHOLDERTON
YOUTH HOSTEL
72a

MENDIP
BUNKHOUSE
72b

Situated on a delightful family owned farm, this 4* youth hostel provides family/child friendly accommodation for groups or individuals. The hostel is 8 miles from Salisbury & 5 miles from Stonehenge. Cooked breakfasts are available & packed lunches & evening meals can be pre-booked.

Guests receive half price admission to the Rare Breeds Farm. Why not also book a vineyard tour & purchase a bottle of home grown sparkling wine? Guests need their own transport.

Larkshall (Mendip Bunkhouse) is the Cerberus Spelaeological Society's headquarters and offers well appointed, modern and comfortable accommodation on The Mendips. It is an ideal base for caving, walking, cycling, climbing, diving at Vobster Quay and for exploring the Somerset countryside. Popular tourist attractions include Wells, Wookey Hole, Cheddar Gorge and the city of Bath. Camping available. Ample parking.

DETAILS

- **Open** - All year
- **Beds** - 70
- **Price/night** - Enquire for prices.

DETAILS

- **Open** - All year. All day.
- **Beds** - 30+ in 4 rooms (plus camping).
- **Price/night** - £10 + 50% for single nights. Minimum of 2 nights at weekends. Enquire for sole use of a bunkroom. Discounts for BMC or BCA members.

CONTACT: Reception
Tel: 01980 629438
info@choldertonyouthhostel.co.uk
www.choldertonyouthhostel.co.uk
Beacon House, Amesbury Road,
Cholderton, Salisbury, Wilts, SP4 0EW

CONTACT:
Tel: 08454 750954
hostelbookings@cerberusspeleo.org.uk
www.cerberusspeleo.org.uk
Larkshall, Fosse Rd. Oakhill, Somerset,
BA3 5HY

BATH YMCA

Bath YMCA offers great value accommodation. Centrally located, all the sights of this World Heritage city are easily reached on foot. With 210 beds, Bath YMCA specialises in making guests feel comfortable. Fully air conditioned lounge with TV, laundry, lockers, football table and WiFi. Couples, families, groups and backpackers all welcome.

DETAILS

- **Open** - All year. All day.
- **Beds** - 210: Dorms: 1x10, 3x12, 1x15, 1x18. Rooms: 7 x quad, 6 x triple, 29 x twin, 5 x double, 9 x single
- **Price/night** - From: dorm £16pp, single £32pp, twin £28pp, double £30pp, double ensuite £40pp, triple £23pp, quad £22pp. Inc breakfast.

CONTACT: Reception
Tel: 01225 325900
stay@ymcabathgroup.org.uk
www.ymcabathgroup.org.uk
International House, Broad Street Place, Bath, BA1 5LH

FULL MOON
BACKPACKERS

74

A live music venue and travellers' hostel at the heart of Bristol's arts and cultural area, Stokes Croft, just 10 minutes' walk from the city centre and bus station. This historic coaching inn is not the place for an early night, as guests get free entry to live music and DJs at the Full Moon's Attic Bar. Beds are available in dorms and private rooms. There is kitchen, common room and a courtyard with plenty of opportunities to get to know people from around the world.

DETAILS

■ **Open** - All year
■ **Beds** - 78: 2xdbl,2xtwin,1x3,1x4,1x5,2 x6,2x8,3x10
■ **Price/night** - From £19pp in a dorm. £40 / £50 for private twin / double.

CONTACT: Reception
Tel: 0117 924 5007
info@fullmoonbristol.co.uk
www.fmbristol.co.uk
1 North St, Stokes Croft,
Bristol, BS1 3PR

KYLE BLUE
BRISTOL HOSTEL BOAT
75

Moored in the heart of Bristol's historic harbour, only a five minute stroll to the city centre. The Kyle Blue Hostel Boat is a converted Dutch Barge with private and shared cabins and a spacious upper deck providing fabulous views of the harbour from its tranquil lounge and well equipped self-catering kitchen. Great for independent travellers or small groups wanting to visit this vibrant city. Sleeping is in various sized cabins with private shower rooms. The Kyle Blue is moored in a residential area so no noise after 11pm.

DETAILS

- **Open** - All year. All day
- **Beds** - 30: 4x1/small dbl, 3x5 1x4 1x7
- **Price/night** - From £29 per person

CONTACT:
Tel: 0117 929 0609
kylebluebristol@gmail.com
www.kylebluebristol.co.uk
Wapping Wharf, Museum Street,
Bristol BS1 6GW

ROCK AND BOWL

The Rock n Bowl Hostel is in the heart of Bristol. It occupies 2 floors of an historic 1930s building with The Lanes, a bowling alley, bar and club venue on the ground floor (hostel guests get great discounts).

With its huge range of rooms there will be a bed to suit your budget. And everyone gets a free breakfast! Facilities include a well equipped large kitchen, lounge with Sky TV including Sky Sports/BT Sports, laundry and free WiFi.

        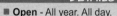

DETAILS

■ **Open** - All year. All day.
■ **Beds** - 144: 1x20, 3x12, 1x10, 3x10 weekly bed dorm, 2x8, 2x6, 3x4, 1x4 female, 1xdouble/twin/3bed, 1xdouble
■ **Price/night** - Dorms from £10pp. Private rooms from £39. Weekly rooms from £90.

CONTACT: The Reception Team
Tel: 0117 325 1980
bookings@rocknbowlmotel.com
www.thelanesbristol.co.uk/hostel
22 Nelson Street, Bristol, BS1 2LE

THE BRISTOL
WING

This brand new hostel, in the historic old police headquarters, is in the heart of the city centre. A mix of private, en suite and dorm rooms makes it ideal for single travellers, couples and families. Close to the bus station, just 20 mins from Bristol Temple Meads and perfectly located for Bristol's best shopping from the independent shops of Park Street & Clifton, to big name brands in Cabot Circus or quirky market stalls in St Nicholas's Market. Meeting rooms are available next door where there is also a conference room and events space which can seat up to 220 people.

DETAILS

- **Open** - All year. All day.
- **Beds** - 88
- **Price/night** - From £18 per person

CONTACT: Reception
Tel: 0117 428 6199
enquiries@thebristolwing.co.uk
www.thebristolwing.co.uk
9 Bridewell Street, Bristol, BS1 2QD

BRISTOL
BACKPACKERS HOSTEL
78a

78b

WETHERDOWN
LODGE

Bristol's most central backpacker hostel. Clean & comfortable beds - mixed/single sex dorms - private rooms - individual bathrooms & free hot showers - free linen - large self-catering kitchen - free tea, coffee & hot chocolate. Late night basement bar - piano & guitar room - DVD lounge - free WiFi - luggage storage room - laundrette.
Run by backpackers for backpackers - No curfew after check in.

An award winning eco-renovation in the heart of the South Downs National Park right on the South Downs Way National Trail. The perfect base for walkers, cyclists, business away-days and family get-togethers. The Lodge offers well appointed self-catering accommodation while the campsite has yurts and secluded woodland pitches. The centre has large grounds with woodland trails and a café. Pubs, shops within 2 miles.

DETAILS

- **Open** - All year. Reception hours 9am -11.30pm (no curfew).
- **Beds** - 90: Bunk bed accommodation in private twin, private triple or 6, 8 and 10 bed dorms.
- **Price/night** - From £19pp. £95 per week. From £39 for private rooms.

CONTACT:
Tel: 0117 925 7900
bristol.backpackers.hostel@gmail.com
www.bristolbackpackers.co.uk
17 St Stephen's Street, Bristol, BS1 1EQ

DETAILS

- **Open** - Hostel and campsite open all year. Yurts closed from Nov to April
- **Beds** - 38: 10 x 3, 4 x 2
- **Price/night** - See sustainability-centre website.

CONTACT: Dan
Tel: 01730 823549
accommodation@sustainability-centre.org
www.sustainability-centre.org
The Sustainability Centre, Droxford Road, East Meon, Hampshire, GU32 1HR

THE PRIVETT
CENTRE
79

In glorious East Hampshire countryside (AONB), The Privett Centre offers low cost, comfortable, short-stay accommodation in a unique rural setting. It has been designed to accommodate small to medium-sized groups who like to have the place to themselves. Outside a large paddock and asphalt playground provide secure and spacious recreational and parking space. It is available for weekday, weekend and day use all year. The Privett Centre is an ideal residential setting for family & friends' get-togethers.

    GROUPS ONLY

DETAILS

- **Open** - All year.
- **Beds** - 29: 1x1, 1x2, 2x4, 1x6, 1x12
- **Price/night** - From £15 pp. Minimum charges apply. (Contact for exact prices).

CONTACT: Mehalah Piedot
Tel: 01256 351555
Privett.Centre@dovehouse.hants.sch.uk
www.privettcentre.org.uk
Church Lane, Privett, Hampshire,
GU34 3PE

GUMBER
CAMPING BARN

A converted Sussex flint barn on a working sheep farm within the National Trust's Slindon Estate, Gumber Camping Barn provides simple overnight accommodation & camping for walkers, horse riders and cyclists, just off the South Downs Way. A tranquil and remote location for you to get away from it all. Just five minutes' walk from Stane Street, the Roman Road that crosses the South Downs Way at Bignor Hill. NO CARS. Not suitable for under fives.

DETAILS

- **Open** - Mar-Oct. Flexible opening hours
- **Beds** - 25: 1x16, 1x5, 1x4 + camping
- **Price/night** - First adult £15. Extra adult £12. Under 18s £6.

CONTACT: Gumber Bookings Team
Tel: 01243 814484
gumberbothy@nationaltrust.org.uk
www.nationaltrust.org.uk/holidays
Gumber Campsite and Camping Barn,
Gumber Farm, Slindon, West Sussex,
BN18 0RN

SLINDON
BUNKHOUSE

81

This bunkhouse on the National Trust Slindon Estate has so much to offer all year round.

In the winter months enjoy the benefit of the wood burner in the lounge, and in the summer enjoy a barbeque in the walled garden.

Perfect for all types of groups and families wanting to get together and enjoy the fabulous South Downs National Park, its surroundings and the miles of footpaths that criss-cross the estate.

DETAILS

- **Open** - All year. All day
- **Beds** - 17, 1x6, 1x10, 1x1
- **Price/night** - 2 nights from £430

CONTACT: National Trust Holidays
Tel: 0344 335 1296
bunkhouses@nationaltrust.org.uk
www.nationaltrust.org.uk/holidays
Slindon Estate Yard, Top Road, Slindon, Arundel, West Sussex, BN18 0RG

SEADRAGON
BACKPACKERS

Seadragon Backpackers is close to the sea front in the seaside resort of Brighton. The kitchen is the focal point of the hostel, where people have been meeting over a cup of tea and a slice of toast since 2006.

There's a sunny airy living room and a choice of private rooms and small dorms, some with a sea view. Use the travel guides and maps provided together with the free WiFi to plan you next adventure.

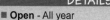

DETAILS

- **Open** - All year
- **Beds** - 20: 1x dbl, 1 x twin, 3x4 (extra 1x4 for groups)
- **Price/night** - From £20pp. Double from £60, Twin from £44 (winter reductions available).

CONTACT: Joe
info@seadragonbackpackers.co.uk
www.seadragonbackpackers.co.uk
36 Waterloo Street, Brighton and Hove,
BN3 1AY

GAVESTON
HALL
83

A former boarding school nestling in beautiful countryside, Gaveston Hall accommodates groups of all sizes. The 100 beds are spread across dorms, private singe/twin rooms & chalets. Set in magnificent grounds with a football field, tennis court, woodland walks and fishing lakes. Outdoor activities can also be provided on-site. Inside there are table tennis & pool tables and an indoor swimming pool (summer only). Room for coach parking.

DETAILS

■ **Open** - All year. Daylight hours
■ **Beds** - 100: Hall: 1x18, 2x16, 2xdbl, 1xtwin, 1xsgl. Chalets: 2x16, 1x15, 1x14
■ **Price/night** - From £18pp. Small extra charge for bedding hire or BYO

CONTACT: Rita Barclay
Tel: 01403 891 431
gavestonhall@outlook.com
www.gavestonhallsussex.com
Nuthurst, Horsham, West Sussex
RH13 6RF

PUTTENHAM
ECO CAMPING BARN

84

Eco project on North Downs Way offering simple overnight accommodation for walkers and cyclists in the Surrey Hills AONB. A converted historic barn with self catering and shared sleeping platforms (possibility of bunkrooms being added in 2020). Pub food in the village. Garden, picnic bench & cycle shed. NO CARS even for off-loading. Stations at Wanborough (3.5 km) & Guildford (7km).

DETAILS
- **Open** - Easter to Oct. Arrive after 5pm leave by 10am. No access 10am-5pm.
- **Beds** - Sleeping platforms for 11.
- **Price/night** - £17 adults; £12 aged 5-17 (accompanied by adult). Sole use by arrangement. £3 `green` voucher if arriving on foot, cycle or public transport.

CONTACT: Bookings
Tel: 01483 811001
bookings@puttenhamcampingbarn.co.uk
www.puttenhamcampingbarn.co.uk
The Street, Puttenham, Nr Guildford,
Surrey, GU3 1AR

HENMAN
BUNKHOUSE

This National Trust owned bunkhouse in the Surrey Hills AONB sleeps up to 16 in 6 and 4 bunk dorms. Well equipped with a self-catering kitchen, large dining table and comfy seating around an open fire.

Walkers can directly access the Greensand Way and other local routes and there are many bridleways and tracks suitable for cycling.

A great place for a group holiday in the countryside only 30 miles from London.

      GROUPS ONLY

DETAILS

■ **Open** - All year. All day except for Christmas and New Year
■ **Beds** - 16: 2x6, 1x4
■ **Price/night** - £225 Friday to Sunday, £180 Monday to Thursday

CONTACT: Henman Bunkhouse
Tel: 01306 712711
leithhill@nationaltrust.org.uk
www.nationaltrust.org.uk/holidays
Broadmoor, Dorking, Surrey, RH5 6JZ

OCTAVIA HILL
BUNKHOUSE

86

Converted from former farm buildings, Octavia Hill Bunkhouse is located on Outridge Farm on the National Trust Toys Hill Estate. Sleeping 10 in two rooms it is the perfect base for families or groups of walkers wanting to explore this lovely part of the Kent Downs Area of Outstanding Natural Beauty.

This bunkhouse has plenty of communal space and a well equipped kitchen for those who want to self-cater. Easily accessible by car, train and bus (the bus stop is just 15 minutes' walk away).

    GROUPS ONLY

DETAILS

- **Open** - All year. All day
- **Beds** - 10: 2x5
- **Price/night** - Min 3 night stay - £788.

CONTACT: National Trust Holidays
Tel: 03443 351296
bunkhouses@nationaltrust.org.uk
www.nationaltrust.org.uk/holidays
Pipers Green Road, Brasted Chart,
Westerham, Kent, TN16 1ND

PALACE FARM
HOSTEL
87

Palace Farm Hostel is a relaxing, flexible 4* hostel on a family run farm.

Situated in the village of Doddington, (which has a pub!), in the North Kent Downs AONB, the area is great for walking, cycling & wildlife. There are ten fully heated en suite rooms sleeping up to 39. Duvets, linen and continental breakfast included.

DETAILS
- **Open** - All year. 8am to 10pm. Flexible, please ask.
- **Beds** - 39: 1x8, 1x6, 2x5 (family room), 1x4, 1x3 and 4x2
- **Price/night** - From £18.50-£40pp (all private en suite rooms). Group reductions.

CONTACT: Graham and Liz Cuthbert
Tel: 01795 886200
info@palacefarm.com
www.palacefarm.com
Down Court Road, Doddington,
Sittingbourne / Faversham,
Kent, ME9 0AU

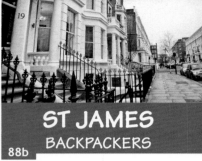

PUBLOVE
@ THE GREEN MAN
88a

ST JAMES
BACKPACKERS
88b

Spend your night above a pub, 5 mins from Paddington Station & experience the real & exciting local London. PubLove@The Green Man, has great transport connections to all the famous sites, 24 hour reception & bar, free WiFi, personal power sockets, bed screens & guest food & drink discounts. You can book by the bed or book a private room. There are friendly bar-staff who like to chat, so ask about places to go and the events happening because there's nothing better then advice from a local.

St James Backpackers is a family-run hostel welcoming global travellers in central London's Earls Court. A great place for people who like to mingle, with a communal dinner each night and a warm community vibe helped along by the lovely staff. Just around the corner from Earl Court Tube station (Zone 1, central London). Free fast WiFi. Free dinner, breakfast and 24hr hot drinks. Lots of space for socialising including a lovely garden and lounge with HD TV.

DETAILS
- **Open** - All year
- **Beds** - 69: 1x3, 3x6, 4x9, 1x12
- **Price/night** - From £15

DETAILS
- **Open** - All year. 24 hour reception,
- **Beds** - 108: Double, twin & triple private rooms (some en suite). Dorms sleeping 4, 6 or 8.
- **Price/night** - From £20, depending on season and room.

CONTACT: The Bar
Tel: 020 7723 7980
greenman@publove.co.uk
www.publove.co.uk/green-man-paddington
The Green Man, 308 Edgware Road, Paddington, London W2 1DY

CONTACT: Reception
Tel: 07450 645573
info@saint-james-hostel.co.uk
www.saint-james-hostel.co.uk
21 Longridge Road, London, SW5 9SB

PARK VILLA
BOUTIQUE HOSTEL 89

Park Villa is a Georgian Regency villa in the heart of the old East End of London. It has a kitchenette, an inviting lounge and free superfast WiFi. The dorms have comfy bunk bed pods and there are en-suite facilities and family rooms.

At the heart of the trendy East End close to the tube, Park Villa makes a great base from which to explore the city of London. Visit for a warm welcome, a comfortable stay and a real home away from home.

DETAILS
■ **Open** - All year, 24 hour reception.
■ **Beds** - 45: 1x2, 1x4, 1x5, 3x6, 2x8
■ **Price/night** - From £19pp midweek, from £30 weekend.

CONTACT: Reception
Tel: 020 8980 1439
WhatsApp: 07496 526 969
reception@parkvilla.co.uk
www.parkvilla.co.uk
51 Grove Road, Bow, London E3 4PE

THE WALRUS
HOSTEL
90

The Walrus is a multi-award-winning hostel above a bar, with staff who are famous for their genuine friendliness and humour. It has a fantastic location only a short 10 minutes' walk from Big Ben and the House of Parliament and all-inclusive hostel prices. It consistently ranks among the top 5 hostels in London. The bar is a crossroads of local and international guests with a laid back atmosphere, a quirky cocktail menu and real ales on tap.

DETAILS

- **Open** - All year. Check in after 2pm, drop off luggage anytime.
- **Beds** - 68: 1x2, 3x4, 4x6, 1x8, 1x22
- **Price/night** - From £13.50 to £24 pp

CONTACT: Reception
Tel: 0207 9284368
thewalrushostel@gmail.com
www.thewalrusbarandhostel.co.uk
The Walrus Bar and Hostel, 172
Westminster Bridge Road,
London, SE1 7RW

GREEN ROOMS
LONDON

Green Rooms is a super affordable arts-led hotel & hostel designed for creatives, young travellers, groups and people who want to make the most of London.

Situated in a beautiful late Art Deco building it offers spacious dormitories, chic doubles and family studios. It is right across the road from Wood Green underground station with direct connection to Central London and Kings Cross in 12 minutes.

DETAILS

- **Open** - All year
- **Beds** - 60: 1x12, 1x4, 2 family apartments, 22 private double rooms.
- **Price/night** - From £19

CONTACT: Reception
Tel: 0208 8885317
info@greenrooms.london
www.greenrooms.london
13-27 Station Road, Wood Green,
London N22 6UW

PUBLOVE
@ THE WHITE FERRY 92

The White Ferry House is a stunning Victorian flat-iron building steeped in history. It provides accommodation in central London, close to Victoria, The Houses of Parliament and Buckingham Palace. In the traditional pub atmosphere you can enjoy chilling out and playing board games, locally sourced drinks and award-winning burgers. There's a 24 hour reception, free WiFi, individual power sockets and guest food & drink discounts. Publove@The White Ferry offers a classic night out and a great location for exploring London by day.

DETAILS
- **Open** - All year.
- **Beds** - 75: 1x3, 1x6, 2x9, 4x12
- **Price/night** - From £15 per person.

CONTACT: The Bar
Tel: 020 7233 6133
whiteferry@publove.co.uk
www.publove.co.uk/white-ferry-victoria
The White Ferry House, 1 Sutherland
Street, London, SW1V 4LD

CLINK78

In the centre of London in a 200 year old courthouse, Clink78 combines original features with modern interior design to create a friendly & unique hostel. In the heart of King's Cross, with easy tube access to the whole city. The friendly team will happily help with your itinerary and provide discounted attraction tickets. Kitchen, games area, TV/film lounge. Meet new people in The ClashBAR.

DETAILS

■ **Open** - All year. 24 hours - no curfew or lockouts.
■ **Beds** - 500: 4-16 bed dorms, triple, twin, single, en suite, cell rooms (for 2)
■ **Price/night** - From £15pp. Bedlinen, WiFi & London walking tour inc. Group discounts.

CONTACT: Maud
Tel: 020 7183 9400
reservations78@clinkhostels.com
www.clinkhostels.com
78 Kings Cross Road, King's Cross,
London, WC1X 9QG

PUBLOVE
@ THE CROWN

94a

PUBLOVE
@ EXMOUTH ARMS

94b

A hip hangout for locals and travellers, The Crown at Battersea has easy-going vibes. Check in and find your bed, then lounge on the cosy sofas with a tipple or get involved with some board games. Newly refurbished in 2018 The Crown is in south-west London on the lively Lavender Street. Hostel beds are in mixed dormitories, with WiFi, fresh linen, duvet and pillow, 24hr bar, reception and security all included. With food and drink discounts for hostel guests, experience the fun and lively atmosphere of PubLove culture in London.

Five minutes' stroll from Euston Station and just 15 minutes' walk from the Eurostar at St Pancras, with The British Museum, Madame Tussauds, Regents Park and many of London's attractions an easy stroll away. PubLove@The Exmouth Arms not only gives you a bed for the night, but also the great atmosphere of a British pub. Complete with pub quizzes every Tuesday, hand crafted burgers and a wide range of drinks including local gins and ales. Explore London by foot in the day with a night of cracking PubLove ahead.

DETAILS

- **Open** - All year.
- **Beds** - 72: 1x3, 6x9, 1x15
- **Price/night** - From £15 per person.

DETAILS

- **Open** - All year
- **Beds** - 65: 1x2, 5x6, 3x8, 1x9
- **Price/night** - From £15 per person.

CONTACT: The Bar
Tel: 020 7738 1122
crown@publove.co.uk
www.publove.co.uk/crown-battersea
PubLove@The Crown,102 Lavender Hill,London, SW11 5RD

CONTACT: Mark
Tel: 020 7387 5440
exmoutharms@publove.co.uk
www.publove.co.uk/exmouth-arms-euston
PubLove @The Exmouth Arms, 1 Starcross Street, London, NW1 2HR

CLINK261

One of London's top backpacker hostels, Clink261 offers simple, comfortable, self-catering accommodation in the city centre. King's Cross is a creative area close to the British Museum, Covent Garden & Camden Market or a short tube ride to Piccadilly Circus & Leicester Square. Guests can go round the corner to Clink78 (see page 93) for entertainment and good value drinks at the ClashBAR.

DETAILS

■ **Open** - All year. All day (except for Xmas) - no curfew or lockouts.
■ **Beds** - 170: 4-6 8-10 & 18 bed dorms, 4 private rooms (up to 2 beds)
■ **Price/night** - From £15pp. Breakfast bookable. Group discounts.

CONTACT: Maud
Tel: 020 7833 9400
reservations261@clinkhostels.com
www.clinkhostels.com
261-265 Gray's Inn Road, King's Cross, London, WC1X 8QT

PUBLOVE
@ STEAM ENGINE

Book a bed upstairs, then relax on one of the snug Chesterfield sofas in this classy British pub in the heart of Waterloo. Everything you need is on hand, 24 hour reception, a beer garden for summer evenings, free WiFi, hand crafted burgers & the best of London's beers & gins. Publove@The Steam Engine is a short walk from London's main attractions. Head to the river to see London in all its glory, Big Ben and the London Eye. Enjoy a classic night out in central London in the heart of British pub culture.

DETAILS

- **Open** - All year
- **Beds** - 80: 1x2, 1x6, 2x9, 3x12, 1x18
- **Price/night** - From £15 per person.

CONTACT: The Bar
Tel: 020 7928 0720
steamengine@publove.co.uk
www.publove.co.uk/steam-engine-waterloo
PubLove@The Steam Engine, 41-42
Cosser Street, London, SE1 7BU

ATLAS
STUDIO ROOMS
97

Atlas Studio Rooms are superbly located in a traditional square in Central London just one min's walk to Paddington Station & 2 mins to Hyde Park. Oxford & Regent Street are 10 min's walk while Big Ben, Houses of Parliament, London Eye & Westminster Abbey are a 20 min walk.

This 72 bed family friendly accommodation offers singles, couples, families & groups of all sizes fantastic value for money. All linen and towels supplied. Airport transfers available on request. Free luggage storage.

DETAILS

- **Open** - All year.
- **Beds** - 72: 1x10, 4x8, 1x6, 5x4, 2x2
- **Price/night** - From £20pp depending on room size.

CONTACT: Reception
Tel: 07477 561947
info@atlasstudiorooms.com
atlasstudiorooms.com
16 Talbot Square, London, W2 1TS

HARLOW
INTERNATIONAL
98a

1912 CENTRE
98b

Harlow International Hostel is in the centre of a landscaped park and is one of the oldest buildings in Harlow. The town of Harlow is your ideal base for exploring London, Cambridge and the best of South East England. The journey time to central London is only 35 minutes from the hostel door and it is the closest hostel to Stansted Airport. National Cycle Route 1 passes the front door. Meals can be provided for groups. There's a children's zoo, orienteering course and outdoor pursuits centre in the park.

The 1912 Centre, in the Harwich Conservation area, is just 50m from the sandy beach & promenade. The centrally heated hostel is the former town fire station. The old engine garage is now the dining and recreational area. The upper floor has 4 cabin style sleeping areas, other beds are on the ground floor & suitable for disabled. Facilities include a fully equipped kitchen, showers & drying room. BYO sleeping or hire duvets.

DETAILS

- **Open** - All year. 8am - 10.30pm (check in 3-10.30pm).
- **Beds** - 30: 2x1, 5x2, 1x4, 1x6, 1x8
- **Price/night** - Please see the website.

DETAILS

- **Open** - All year. All day. Except 24th-27th December.
- **Beds** - 26: 3x6, 2x2, 1x4.
- **Price/night** - 1 night £290, 2 nights £540, 5 nights £1075, 7 nights £1350. Other prices on application.

CONTACT: Richard Adams
Tel: 01279 421702
mail@h-i-h.co.uk
www.h-i-h.co.uk
13 School Lane, Harlow, Essex, CM20 2QD

CONTACT: Debbie Hill
Tel: 01255 552010
info@harwichconnexions.co.uk
www.harwichconnexions.co.uk
Cow Lane, Off Kings Quay Street, Harwich CO12 3ES

OLD BROODER
BUNKHOUSE

Comfy, farm self-catering in rural Suffolk. Sleeps 22 in five bedrooms, including a restored Shepherd's Hut. Mix of oak bunks/conventional beds. Relax in cosy sitting room; BBQ, ping-pong, croquet & badminton; explore the farm, picnic in a meadow. 20 bikes included in hire or kayak down the River Stour. Go Ape, visit castles, coast, historic towns & houses. Larger groups can also book the Tudor Barn (see page 100).

      GROUPS ONLY

DETAILS

- **Open** - Check booking arrangements
- **Beds** - 22: 3x2, 2x8
- **Price/night** - W/ends: 2nt min from £1400. 3nts Bk Hols £1900. 2nt m/week from £900. Ask for a quote for small groups or 1-night stays.

CONTACT: Juliet Hawkins
Tel: 01787 247235
hawkins@thehall-milden.co.uk
www.thehall-milden.co.uk
The Hall, Milden, Lavenham, Sudbury,
Suffolk CO10 9NY

TUDOR BARN

The Tudor Barn offers unique group accommodation on an environmentally friendly working farm in rural Suffolk. Sleeping 23 (singles/doubles/4 posters & truckles) in 4 private rooms + the huge space of the Tudor Barn where you can also feast & relax. The perfect base for group celebrations, reunions or activity breaks. Bikes and Tudor costumes are included. Larger parties can also stay at the Old Brooder Bunkhouse on the same site (see page 99).

      GROUPS ONLY

DETAILS

- **Open** - Check booking arrangements
- **Beds** - 23+: 3x2, 1x1, 1x16. (+cots)
- **Price/night** - W/ends: 2nt £1,500 to £2,640. 2nt midweek £1,150 ask for quotes for small groups/1 night stays.

CONTACT: Juliet Hawkins
Tel: 01787 247235
hawkins@thehall-milden.co.uk
www.thehall-milden.co.uk
The Hall, Milden, Lavenham, Sudbury, Suffolk CO10 9NY

CHELLINGTON
CENTRE

A unique and memorable venue for group stays. Situated in the beautiful Bedfordshire countryside with amazing views across the Great River Ouse, it's easily accessible from the M1 but a world apart. The converted 12th century church can sleep 30 in bunkrooms, with modern facilities, an industrial style kitchen for self-catering and two breakout rooms.
Youth group discounts available.

DETAILS

- **Open** - All year
- **Beds** - 30: 2x5, 5x4
- **Price/night** - Youth groups: week night £385, weekend (Fri&Sat exit by 2pm Sunday) £840, Other Groups: week night £440, weekend £1050.

CONTACT: Claire or Scott
Tel: 01234 720726
admin@chellington.org
www.chellington.org
The Chellington Centre, St Nicholas Church, Felmersham Road, Carlton, Bedford MK43 7NA

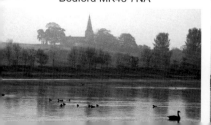

CHILTERNS
BUNKHOUSE

Located on the National Trust's Ashridge Estate in the heart of the Chilterns Area of Outstanding Natural Beauty, this bunkhouse provides rustic, basic accommodation in two restored barns located amongst the woodlands and grassland of the estate.

A well equipped self-catering kitchen, lounge and outdoor eating area make it perfect for self-catering groups whilst the nearby picture postcard village of Aldbury has two pubs and a shop. There is no mobile reception at the bunkhouse.

        GROUPS ONLY

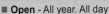

DETAILS
- **Open** - All year. All day
- **Beds** - 16: 2x8
- **Price/night** - From £250

CONTACT: National Trust Holidays
Tel: 03443 351296
bunkhouses@nationaltrust.org.uk
www.nationaltrust.org.uk/holidays
Outwood Kiln, Aldbury, Tring,
Hertfordshire, HP23 5SE

COURT HILL
CENTRE

103

Just 2 miles south of Wantage, and only a few steps from the historic Ridgeway National Trail, Court Hill Centre enjoys breathtaking views over the Vale of the White Horse. Reclaimed barns surround a pretty courtyard garden. Providing accommodation for families, groups and individuals, the centre offers evening meals, breakfasts and picnic lunches.

There is a beautiful high-roofed dining room which retains the atmosphere of the old barn. A meeting/class-room, camping and self-catering available.

DETAILS

■ **Open** - All year. To check availability please call 01235 760253.
■ **Beds** - 59: 1x15,1x9,1x6,1x5,6x4,1x2
■ **Price/night** - From £22.50. U18 £15.50

CONTACT: Reception
Tel: 01235 760253
info@courthill.org.uk
www.courthill.org.uk
Letcombe Regis, Wantage, OX12 9NE

CROFT FARM
WATERPARK
104a

Just outside Tewkesbury in the scenic River Avon Valley, with it's own lake. Accommodation is in cabins, a pod village, chalets & camping. Great for touring the Cotswolds, Malverns, Bredon Hill & the Forest of Dean. A wide range of watersports, activities & tuition are on offer. A footpath meanders through the meadow to the River Avon and free river fishing is available to guests.

DETAILS
■ **Open** - All year. 9am-9pm.
■ **Beds** - 216: Chalets: quad x32, twin x8. Cabins (sleep 8) x5. Pod quad x8
■ **Price/night** - Pod/Chalet (4 pers) £50 (£65 for 1 night). Chalet (twin room) £50 (£65/1 night). Cabin (8 pers en suite) £120 (£140/1 night)

CONTACT: Martin Newell
Tel: 01684 772321 or 07736 036967
info@croftfarmwaterpark.com
www.croftfarmwaterpark.com
Bredons Hardwick, Near Tewkesbury,
Gloucestershire GL20 7EE

YE OLD FERRIE INN
BUNKHOUSE
104b

This beautiful riverside pub has been standing on the banks of the River Wye since the 15th century. With charming traditional features, warming open fires and stunning views across the valley, Ye Old Ferrie Inn is the ideal base for your exploration of the Wye Valley. Ye Old Ferrie Inn Bunkhouse, adjoining the inn, is the perfect place for you to hang up your rucksack, kick off your walking boots and relax. Popular with canoeists, walkers and climbers. If you don't fancy self-catering there is B&B in the inn.

DETAILS
■ **Open** - All year. All day.
■ **Beds** - 20:1x14, 1x6 + dbl B&B rooms.
■ **Price/night** - From £15 per person. For sole use please ring to enquire.

CONTACT: Jamie
Tel: 01600 890 232
hello@yeoldferrieinn.com
www.yeoldferrieinn.com
Ferrie Lane, Symonds Yat West,
Herefordshire HR9 6BL

WOODSIDE LODGES
BUNKHOUSE
105

Woodside Lodges Bunkhouse sits in a landscaped park with pools & wild flower meadows, along with Scandinavian self-catering lodges, a campsite and camping pods. The bunkhouse offers 5 self-catering units. Guests enjoy private rooms but share the campsite shower block. Close to the Herefordshire Trail, Malvern Hills & the Forest of Dean it's ideal for walkers, cyclists & nature lovers.

DETAILS

■ **Open** - All year. All day.
■ **Beds** - 16: 1x2, 2x3, 2x4 (max 20 using camp beds)
■ **Price/night** - From £12.50 based on 4 sharing. Sole use of rooms. Phone/check website for full prices. £5 per pet.

CONTACT: Woodside Lodges Country Park
Tel: 01531 670269
info@woodsidelodges.co.uk
www.woodsidelodges.co.uk
Woodside Lodges, Falcon Lane, Ledbury, Herefordshire, HR8 2JN

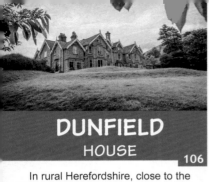

DUNFIELD
HOUSE

106

In rural Herefordshire, close to the Welsh border, Dunfield House provides accommodation for groups of up to 95 with sole use of the house, stables, parkland & swimming pool. From November to March the house & stables can also be hired individually.

The house provides fully catered accommodation & the stables have a self-catering kitchen. A great choice for school, youth, music or church groups, training courses & family get-togethers.

     GROUPS ONLY

DETAILS

- **Open** - All year. All day.
- **Beds** - 95: main house 73, stables: 22
- **Price/night** - Sole hire of site from £25pp fully catered. Stables (sleeping 22) self-catering from £400 per night.

CONTACT: The Reception Team
Tel: 01544 230563
info@dunfieldhouse.org.uk
www.dunfieldhouse.org.uk
Kington, Herefordshire. HR5 3NN

LUDLOW MASCALL
CENTRE

A beautiful Victorian building in the heart of Ludlow, extended to provide en-suite accommodation with twin rooms, a family room, and a room designed for those with limited mobility. Within walking distance of restaurants, shops and pubs and near to the Shropshire Hills and Mortimer Forest with miles of stunning landscapes to explore. Fresh towels, bedlinen, complimentary toiletries, tea- and coffee-making facilities, parking and WiFi included. Breakfasts available.

DETAILS

- **Open** - All year, not Xmas & New Year
- **Beds** - 19: 1x4, 7x2, 1x1.
- **Price/night** - Family room (4 beds) from £72. Twin room from £54. Single room from £36.

CONTACT:
Tel: 01584 873882
info@ludlowmascallcentre.co.uk
www.ludlowmascallcentre.co.uk
Lower Galdeford, Ludlow,
Shropshire SY8 1RZ

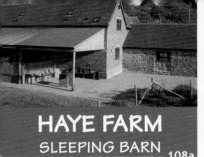

HAYE FARM
SLEEPING BARN
108a

FOXHOLES
108b
CASTLE BUNKHOUSE

This bunkhouse on a working farm has a fully equipped self-catering kitchen, dining room and lounge. Enjoy the quiet rural location on the covered decking, patio (with BBQ) and lawn. The nearby Wye Forest is one of the largest remaining ancient forests in England. On the Worcestershire Way and close to the Severn Way and Mercian Way (NCN route 45) at Bewdley (1 mile). The West Midland Safari Park and Severn Valley Railway are also very close.

Foxholes Castle Bunkhouse, is situated within a relaxed, family-run campsite, with glorious views of South West Shropshire's beautiful hills. Just a few minutes' walk from the Shropshire Way, Offa's Dyke Path and the Sustrans cycle network, it is the perfect base for walkers, cyclists, photographers, families or couples. The lively town of Bishops Castle with its pubs, cafés, restaurants and take-aways is just a 10 minute walk away. In addition to the bunkhouse there are 2 cabins nearby. The Datcha sleeps 6 and the Eco cabin sleeps 8.

DETAILS
- **Open** - All year. 24 hour access.
- **Beds** - 15: 1x2, 1x3, 1x4, 1x6
- **Price/night** - From £20pp. Book a bed in a dorm, a private room or sole use of the whole barn. Visit website for prices.

CONTACT: Stuart Norgrove
Tel: 7732489195
enquiries@haye-farm.co.uk
www.haye-farm.co.uk
Haye Farm, Ribbesford, Bewdley,
Worcestershire, DY12 2TP

DETAILS
- **Open** - All year.
- **Beds** - 7
- **Price/night** - £15 pp. Sole use: £70

CONTACT: Adam Smith/Wendy Jones
Tel: 01588 638924
foxholes.castle@googlemail.com
www.foxholes-castle.co.uk
Foxholes Camping, Montgomery Rd,
Bishops Castle, Shropshire, SY9 5HA

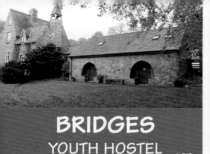

BRIDGES
YOUTH HOSTEL
109a

109b

WOMERTON FARM
BUNKHOUSE

Tucked away in the tranquil Shropshire hills, close to Long Mynd & Stiperstones, Bridges Hostel is an ideal spot for walkers with the Shropshire Way passing close by. It is also handy for the End to End cycle route and good mountain biking routes. The hostel has a good kitchen, lounge with wood fire, drying room, shop and a large garden. Home cooked, home grown three course evening meals are available. Camping is available and there is a pub nearby.

Womerton Farm Bunkhouse sits right next to the Long Mynd in the heart of the Shropshire Hills. It sleeps 8 with a well appointed kitchen & living area. It is just 3 miles from Church Stretton, 12 miles from Shrewsbury & 15 miles from Ludlow. Local attractions include Acton Scott Working Farm Museum, Stokesay Castle & Museum of Lost Content. Well behaved dogs allowed.

DETAILS

- **Open** - All year. Reception open 8-10 am & 5-10 pm. Hostel closes at 11pm.
- **Beds** - 38: 2x4 en suite, 1x6 or 8, 1x10, 1x12 plus camping
- **Price/night** - From £22. Discounts for YHA. Camping £10.

CONTACT: Bridges Youth Hostel
Tel: 01588 650656
mickandgill@btconnect.com
Ratlinghope, Shrewsbury, Shropshire,
SY5 0SP

DETAILS

- **Open** - All year. All day. Closed from 11 am to 4pm on change over days.
- **Beds** - 8: 1x6 bunks + dble sofa bed.
- **Price/night** - Sole use: £80 Xmas/ New Year & Easter-Sept. £60 off peak. Discounts for 4+ nights & mid-week.

CONTACT: Ruth or Tony
Tel: 01694 751260
ruth@womerton-farm.co.uk
www.womerton-farm.co.uk
Womerton Farm, All Stretton, Church
Stretton, Shropshire, SY6 6LJ

ALL STRETTON
BUNKHOUSE
110

All Stretton Bunkhouse offers comfortable, cosy, self-catering accommodation for individuals and groups of up to 10. It has easy access to the Long Mynd with walks and bike rides for all levels. It is within easy reach of the busy town of Church Stretton and just 10 minutes' walk from the local pub. There's a well equipped kitchen, a shower, two toilets and a tumble dryer. Sole use bookings may bring dogs.

DETAILS

- **Open** - All year. Winter 4pm-10.30am. Summer 5pm-10.30am.
- **Beds** - 10: 2x4, 1x2
- **Price/night** - £21, children half price. £1 pppn discount for arriving without a vehicle.

CONTACT: Frankie Goode; Mike Goode
Tel: 01694 722593 or 07815 517482
info@allstrettonbunkhouse.co.uk
www.allstrettonbunkhouse.co.uk
Meadow Green, Batch Valley, All Stretton, Shrops, SY6 6JW

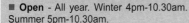

STOKES BARN
BUNKHOUSES

On top of Wenlock Edge AONB in the heart of Shropshire, Stokes Barn has two bunkhouses with comfortable, centrally heated, dormitory accommodation. Perfect for corporate groups, walkers, field study, schools, stag/hen parties or reunions with friends/family. Ironbridge World Heritage Site is 6 miles away. Much Wenlock is within walking distance with shops, pubs & sports facilities.

        GROUPS ONLY

DETAILS

- **Open** - All year. All day.
- **Beds** - Threshing Barn 28: 1x12,1x10,1x6 Granary 16: 1x10,1x4,1x2
- **Price/night** - Prices per min 2 nights: Barn: £560 midweek, £910 weekend. Granary: £398 midweek, £615 weekend. Both units weekend 2 nights: £1365.

CONTACT: Helen
Tel: 01952 727491
info@stokesbarn.co.uk
www.stokesbarn.co.uk
Stokes Barn, Newtown Farm, Much Wenlock, Shropshire, TF13 6DB

DUDMASTON
BUNKHOUSE
112a

SPRINGHILL
FARM BUNKHOUSE
112b

This new bunkhouse will be opening on the Dudmaston Estate in summer 2020.

Operated by the National Trust Dudmaston Bunkhouse is 4 miles S/E of Bridgnorth and will provide ideal accommodation for groups of up to 16 in 8 bedrooms. It has self-catering facilities, a large dining/meeting room & a soft seating area. The bunkhouse is perfect for groups of family/friends, walkers and clubs. Dudmaston has lots to offer with managed woodlands, beautiful walks, tranquil pools with plenty of wildlife.

Part of a Welsh hill farm on the Wales/ Shropshire border at 1475ft above sea level, with beautiful views over the Ceiriog Valley and Berwyn Mountains. Great for walking, riding, cycling, team building, meetings, or just to relax. There is a heated games and lecture room. The bunkhouse has under-floor heating, entrance hall, drying room, large self catering kitchen, dining area & lounge. The patio and lawn have a BBQ and hot tub. Horse riding and archery on site. Horses and pets welcome on request.

DETAILS

- **Open** - All year: Opening August 2020.
- **Beds** - 16: 8x2
- **Price/night** - To be confirmed.

CONTACT: National Trust Holidays
Tel: 0344 335 1296
bunkhouses@nationaltrust.org.uk
www.nationaltrust.org.uk/holidays
Dudmaston Estate, Quatford, Bridgnorth, Shropshire, WV15 6QR

DETAILS

- **Open** - All year by arrangement.
- **Beds** - Bunkhouse: 25, Cottages: 2x6
- **Price/night** - £20pp (including bedding but not towels)

CONTACT: Sue Benbow
Tel: 01691 718406
sue@springhillfarm.co.uk
www.springhillfarm.co.uk
Springhill Farm, Selattyn, Oswestry, Shropshire, SY10 7NZ

FORDHALL FARM

STRAWBALE BUNKHOUSE

113

Fordhall Organic Farm, near Market Drayton, is England's first community owned farm. The Straw Bale Bunkhouse is ideal for schools, retreats & groups.

This unique property has exceptional environmental credentials & is designed to encourage people to get immersed in nature & enjoy the wonderful landscape. Educational sessions, linked to elements of the National Curriculum, can be arranged or you can host your own retreat or event.

DETAILS

- **Open** - All year excl. 25 Dec - 1 Jan.
- **Beds** - 25: 2x10, 1x3, 1x2 + yurt
- **Price/night** - From £100 for educational users

CONTACT: Marie Gibson
Tel: 01630 638696
marie.gibson@fordhallfarm.com
www.fordhallfarm.com
Tern Hill Road, Market Drayton,
Shropshire, TF9 3PS

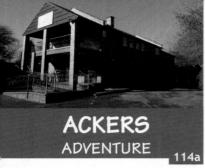

ACKERS
ADVENTURE
114a

BIRMINGHAM
BACKPACKERS
114b

Ackers Residential Centre (ARC) is a purpose built accommodation centre set in 70 acres of semi rural land just 2 miles from the centre of Birmingham. Perfect for The Sea Life Centre, Cadbury World, Thinktank, The Bull Ring shopping centre, National Motorcycle Museum & the NEC. With 9 sleeping rooms, a fully equipped self-catering kitchen, dining area and a rec room with TV, DVD, games and comfy seating. Ackers Adventure provide instructor led outdoor activities on site which can be incorporated into your stay.

Birmingham Central Backpackers is Birmingham's first Independent Hostel! Run by travellers for travellers.

A minute's walk from the National Express coach station and Airport buses and 7 mins from New Street train station. Oozing with quirky colourful character and friendly staff this is THE base for exploring the brilliance of Birmingham.

DETAILS
- **Open** - All year
- **Beds** - 80: 11 rooms of 4-8 beds 1x3, 3x2, 2x1 + pod dorm
- **Price/night** - From £13 to £26 depending on room and season. Includes a light breakfast.

DETAILS
- **Open** - All year.
- **Beds** - 26: 4x4, 5x2
- **Price/night** - Enquire for price.

CONTACT: Triona Boden
Tel: 0121 772 5111
bookings@ackers-adventure.co.uk
www.ackers-adventure.co.uk
Ackers (ARC), Waverley Canal Basin,
Small Heath, Birmingham, B10 0DQ

CONTACT: Reception
Tel: 0121 6430033
Mobile: 07756 829970
info@birminghamcentralbackpackers.com
birminghambackpackers.com
58 Coventry Street, Digbeth,
Birmingham, B5 5NH

IGLOO
HYBRID

115

On Market Square, right in the centre of Nottingham, Igloo offers great value and comfort. Decorated using up-cycled furniture and street art murals, with a self-catering kitchen, free WiFi, power showers, lockers, lounge, outdoor courtyard and laundry facilities. The Pods & Annexe offer further rooms with the same standard. The Igloo SHED is our newly addition with ensuite room.

DETAILS

- **Open** - All year. All day. Reception open 7am-1am Sun-Fri, 24hrs Sat.
- **Beds** - 58: singles, twins, doubles, triples, quads and family rooms.
- **Price/night** - Dorms: from £19pp. Singles from £29. Triples from £48. Quads from £64. Ensuite from £36.

CONTACT: Igloo Hybrid
Tel: 0115 9483822
hybrid@igloohostel.co.uk
www.igloohostel.co.uk
Igloo Hybrid, 4-6 Eldon Chambers,
Wheeler Gate, Nottingham, NG1 2NS

HUNSTANTON
BACKPACKERS & YHA
116a

DEEPDALE
BACKPACKERS
116b

This family-run, family friendly licensed hostel is ideal for schools (classroom available) & groups as sole use or for families & individuals in private rooms. Close to the beach, town centre, Sealife sanctuary, cliff walks and buses serving the Norfolk Coast. Perfect for walking, cycling, birding and fun on the beach. Food served or self-cater in the kitchen. Enjoy sea views from the garden patio.

Deepdale Backpackers offers a range of comfortable self-catering rooms with private en suite shower/toilet facilities, plus single sex dorms. All bedding is provided, just BYO towels. With underfloor heating throughout, laundry & drying facilities, all rooms have shared access to a large well equipped kitchen, communal dining area and living room.

DETAILS

■ **Open** - All year. 8-10am, 5-9.30pm.
■ **Beds** - 48: 1x dbl, 2x3, 4x4, 1x5/6, 2x6/8, 1 grd floor 2 bed. Some en suite.
■ **Price/night** - Prices from: Dorms £24, 2 bed £55, 4 bed £80. Ask re multi night discounts, family rooms, sole use & schools/groups full board packages.

CONTACT: Neal or Alison Sanderson
Tel: 01485 532061 or 07771 804831
hunstantonhostel@talktalk.net
www.norfolkbeachholidays.co.uk
15-17 Avenue Road, Hunstanton,
Norfolk, PE36 5BW

DETAILS

■ **Open** - All year. All day. Collect key from Deepdale Visitor Information Centre
■ **Beds** - 50: 5 x dbl, 1 twin, 1 quad, 1 family quad, 2 female dorms, 2 male dorms
■ **Price/night** - From £12 in a shared dorm room. From £30 twin/double room.

CONTACT: Deepdale Backpackers & Camping
Tel: 01485 210256
stay@deepdalebackpackers.co.uk
www.deepdalebackpackers.co.uk
Deepdale Farm, Burnham Deepdale,
Norfolk, PE31 8DD

DEEPDALE
GROUPS HOSTEL

117

Deepdale Groups Hostel is at the heart of Burnham Deepdale on the beautiful North Norfolk Coast. The Groups Hostel offers comfortable, self-catering accommodation for groups.

Sleeping up to 18 people in 4 bedrooms, it is perfect for friends, larger family gathering, clubs or reunions. A great base for a walking break, cycling tour or for bird/wildlife watching groups. The knowledgeable staff will give advice and share their passion for the area.

DETAILS

- **Open** - All year. All day. Collect key from Deepdale Visitor Information Centre
- **Beds** - 18: 2x6, 1x4, 1x2
- **Price/night** - From £234 (18 people)

CONTACT: Deepdale Groups Hostel
Tel: 01485 210256
stay@deepdalebackpackers.co.uk
www.deepdalebackpackers.co.uk
Deepdale Farm, Burnham Deepdale,
Norfolk, PE31 8DD

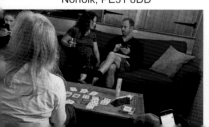

TOWER
WINDMILL

Built in 1816 and last used as a working mill in 1914, this National Trust bunkhouse has panoramic views of the countryside and the Norfolk coastline.

A perfect venue and location for groups of family and friends to get together and explore the local beaches and miles of public footpaths. Featuring a well equipped ground floor kitchen, sitting/dining area, a third floor library and large enclosed garden. BYO bedding and linen.

DETAILS

- **Open** - All year.
- **Beds** - 19: 2x8, 1x twin, 1x single
- **Price/night** - 3 night weekend from £504-£984. 7 nights from £790-£1420

CONTACT: National Trust Holidays
Tel: 0344 335 1296
bunkhouses@nationaltrust.org.uk
www.nationaltrust.org.uk/holidays
Tower Windmill, Tower Road, Burnham
Overy Staithe, Norfolk, PE31 8JB

BRANCASTER
ACTIVITY CENTRE
119

This National Trust Grade II listed flint cottage lies in the picturesque harbour of Brancaster Staithe on the North Norfolk Coast. With stunning sea views across the beautiful marshes. Groups of up to 22 or 48 can be accommodated (sole occupancy). Self-cater in the well equipped kitchen, or eat out in nearby pubs and cafés. The upstairs 'snug' has a TV and woodburner and there is a garden with seating and gas BBQ. Perfect for sailing, walking, kite surfing, bird watching & the Norfolk Coast Path.

        GROUPS ONLY

DETAILS

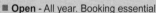

- **Open** - All year. Booking essential
- **Beds** - 48:1x8, 1x7, 2x6, 3x5, 1x4, 1x2
- **Price/night** - From £744 (2 nights/22 beds/low) to £1580 (2 nts/48 beds/high)

CONTACT: National Trust Holidays
Tel: 0344 335 1296
bunkhouses@nationaltrust.org.uk
www.nationaltrust.org.uk/holidays
Dial House, Harbour Way, Brancaster Staithe, Kings Lynn, Norfolk PE31 8BW

OLD RED LION

The medieval walled town of Castle Acre is on the Peddars Way ancient track/long distance path. This former pub, continues to serve travellers who seek refreshment and repose. Stay in private rooms or dorms (bedding/linen supplied). There are quiet communal areas and 2 large areas suitable for group activities.

DETAILS

■ **Open** - All year. All day. Arrival times by arrangement.

■ **Beds** - 22: 1x8, 1x6, 1x double, 2x double en suite, 2x twin

■ **Price/night** - Double ensuite £75. Wet room (ground floor) £75/Sgle occ.£55. Double £65/Sgle occ £45. Twin £55/Sgle occ £40. Discounts for 2+ nights. Dorms £25. B/fast, bedding, towel included.

CONTACT: Alison Loughlin
Tel: 01760 755557
oldredlion@yahoo.co.uk
www.oldredlion.org.uk
Old Red Lion, Bailey Street, Castle Acre,
Norfolk, PE32 2AG

VIKING
CENTRE

Situated in the village of Claxby in the Lincolnshire Wolds Area of Outstanding Natural Beauty, this low cost hostel has a well equipped kitchen, Wifi and a good sized communal area. Within easy reach of Lincoln, Gainsborough, Scunthorpe and Grimsby. The perfect location for: walking, cycling, field studies, outdoor pursuits, educational activities and conservation projects. Popular with family groups, schools, scouts, guides, walkers, cycling groups and other organisations. Ideal for groups wanting a break in beautiful rural surroundings.

GROUPS ONLY

DETAILS

- **Open** - All year
- **Beds** - 20: 2x4, 2x6
- **Price/night** - £90 per night per group

CONTACT: Susannah Boulton
Tel: 07903 584114
info@thevikingcentre.com
www.thevikingcentre.com
Pelham Road, Claxby, Market Rasen,
Lincolnshire LN8 3YR

HULL TRINITY
BACKPACKERS

122

In the heart of historic Hull this hostel is aimed at the individual traveller, small groups, cyclists and families. Perfect for visiting Hull's art exhibitions & attractions, like the newly opened Hull Bonus Arena. Family and en-suite rooms, self-catering kitchen and vibrant coffee lounge. Great for visiting the East Yorkshire Coast, historic Beverley and York. Daily ferries to Belgium and the Netherlands put Europe on the doorstep.

DETAILS

- **Open** - All year (not Xmas & New Year). 3-10pm check in, flexible with notice.
- **Beds** - 24: 1x6, 2x4, 1x4 en suite, 3 x single/twin. Flexibility for groups.
- **Price/night** - £19pp (dorm), £30pp (single). £39 (twin). Longer stay flexibility.

CONTACT: Glenn Gavin
Tel: 07853 000474 or 01482 223229
hulltrinitybackpackers@gmail.com
hulltrinitybackpackers.com
51/52 Market Place Kingston Upon Hull
HU1 1RQ

SHINING CLIFF
HOSTEL
123a

With its own crags, streams, lakes & 100-acres of mature woodland, Shining Cliff Hostel has nature on its doorstep. Access is half a mile from the nearest parking area along a rough woodland footpath. Paths lead through the woods to the A6 at Ambergate (20 mins' walk) which has a food shop, pub, buses and trains to Derby. The hostel is ideal for a wide range of groups wishing to enjoy time away in a peaceful woodland setting.

DETAILS

- **Open** - All year.
- **Beds** - 20: 1x4, 2x6, 2x2
- **Price/night** - Sole use £280 pn. Individuals & small groups (weekdays only) £15 pp, children (5-15) £7.50, under 5s free.

CONTACT: Kate Tuck
Tel: 07794 268059
shiningcliffhostel@yahoo.com
shiningcliffhostel.co.uk
Jackass Lane, Alderwasley, DE56 2RE

MOORSIDE FARM
BUNKHOUSE
123b

A 300-year-old farmhouse set 1200 feet up in the beautiful Derbyshire/ Staffordshire Peak District National Park. Five miles from historic Buxton and a perfect base for all the Peak District has to offer. The 2 sleeping areas sleep 14 and 6 - perfect for a small group or family. A 3 course breakfast and optional packed lunch / substantial evening meal are provided. Hot drinks can be made in the small kitchen. No self-catering facilities. Ample parking space.

GROUPS ONLY

DETAILS

- **Open** - All year. 24 hours.
- **Beds** - 20: 1 x 14, 1 x 6
- **Price/night** - Full board (b/fast, packed lunch, eve meal) £40pp, B&B £30pp. Groups only (Min booking of 4 people).

CONTACT: Charlie
Tel: 01298 83406
charliefutcher@aol.com
www.moorsidefarm.com
Hollinsclough, Longnor, Buxton, Derbyshire, SK17 0RF

GLENORCHY
CENTRE

124

The Glenorchy Centre is on the edge of the Peak District National Park in the historic market town of Wirksworth. The High Peak Trail for walking, pony trekking & cycling, as well as Black Rocks for bouldering & climbing are within two miles. Nearby Cromford has Arkwright's mills, a World Heritage Site, & Cromford Canal. Suitable for self-catering groups, the accommodation is well appointed with a spacious multi-purpose room & separate dining room.

GROUPS ONLY

DETAILS

- **Open** - March to early Dec. 24 hours.
- **Beds** - 26: 1x12, 1x8, 1x4, 1x2
- **Price/night** - Mon-Thurs £1015 (4nts); Fri-Sun £635 (2nts); Sat-Sat £1450 (7nts) Small grps £20pp. 1 nt: min charge £420.

CONTACT: The Secretary
Tel: 01629 824323
secretary@glenorchycentre.org.uk
www.glenorchycentre.org.uk
Chapel Lane, Wirksworth, Derbyshire, DE4 4FF

MATLOCK
GLAMPING ROOMS 125

Set in the heart of the historic spar town of Matlock, these newly renovated 'Glamping Rooms' ooze style and comfort.

On site and available to guests, by prior arrangement, is Designate's cosy bar with open fires, home cooked food and a fully licensed party venue complete with beach garden. The two rooms are self contained, each with a shower room, kitchenette and beds for up to 6 guests.

DETAILS

- **Open** - All year.
- **Beds** - 12 : 2 x 6
- **Price/night** - Two people £60 midweek, £75 weekends. Extra guests/ single bed : £15pp

CONTACT: Kirsty or Andy
Tel: 07790 088842
sales@designateproducts.co.uk
www.homeofhandmade.co.uk
Designate, 6 Rutland Street, Matlock, Derbyshire, DE4 3GN

ILAM
BUNKHOUSE

The former 19th century stable block of Ilam Hall in the Peak District National Park close to Dovedale. Now managed by the National Trust and providing high quality group accommodation.

Each bunk has a locker, night light and plug socket. The sociable main living area has a large dining table with benches, an open plan kitchen and large comfortable sofas. Explore the limestone hills, dales, rivers and woodland of the picturesque White Peak.

     **GROUPS ONLY**

DETAILS

- **Open** - All year. All day.
- **Beds** - 16: 2x6, 1x4
- **Price/night** - From £416 for 2 nights mid week. Minimum bookings apply. Dogs: £15/dog/stay. Max 2 dogs.

CONTACT: National Trust Holidays
Tel: 03443 351296
bunkhouses@nationaltrust.org.uk
www.nationaltrust.org.uk/holidays
Ilam Park, Ilam, nr Ashbourne, DE6 2AZ

ALSTONEFIELD
CAMPING BARN
127

Close to Dovedale, the Manifold Valley Cycle Trail, Carsington Water, AltonTowers and the Roaches Rocks (great for climbers). Ideal for quiet group get-togethers/parties, families, cyclists, walkers, DofE, Scouts, school groups and team building. Camping in the comfort of a remote cosy barn with log burning stove, fully plumbed in toilet and hand wash basin. No electric and no distractions, it is the perfect place to switch off from the hassles of a hectic life. BYO all camping equipment.

DETAILS

- **Open** - All year. All day apart from Christmas and New Year.
- **Beds** - 12: BYO sleeping mats & bags
- **Price/night** - £9.50pp, £114 sole use.

CONTACT: Robert or Teresa Flower
Tel: 01335 310349
gateham.grange@btinternet.com
www.gatehamgrange.co.uk
Gateham Grange, Alstonefield,
Ashbourne, Derbys. DE6 2FT

BUTTERTON
CAMPING BARNS
128

Fenns Farm Accommodation can offer guests accommodation to suit all budgets. It consists of four properties, Waterslacks Camping barn sleeping 15, Wills 'Glamping' Barn sleeping 6 and two holiday cottages, Fenns & Foggs' Barn both sleeping 7.

All the accommodation is situated on the edge of the Peak District village of Butterton, in walking distance of the local pub and the Manifold Valley.

DETAILS
- **Open** - All year. All day
- **Beds** - Waterslacks:15. Wills:6. Fenns:7. Foggs:7
- **Price/night** - Waterslacks from £127, Wills from £90, Fenns Barn from £100.

CONTACT: Jason and Michelle
Tel: 07708 200282
fennsfarmaccommodation@gmail.com
www.peakdistrictbarns.co.uk
Fenns Farm, Wetton Road, Butterton, Leek, Staffordshire, ST13 7ST

SHEEN
BUNKHOUSE

Sheen Bunkhouse is in a quiet corner of the Peak District, close to the beautiful Dove and Manifold valleys. It has a well equipped self-catering kitchen, lounge, two bunkrooms and separate toilets & showers.

The Manifold Track, Tissington Trail and High Peak Trail give easy access to beautiful countryside, ideal for families and cyclists. Dovedale and the moors offer stunning walking. Buxton, Leek and Bakewell are within 12 miles and Alton Towers is 20 minutes away by car.

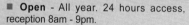

DETAILS

■ **Open** - All year. 24 hours access, reception 8am - 9pm.
■ **Beds** - 14: 1x8, 1x6
■ **Price/night** - From: Adults £17 U16s £12

CONTACT: Jean or Graham Belfield
Tel: 01298 84501
grahambelfield11@gmail.com
Peakstones, Sheen, Derbys, SK17 0ES

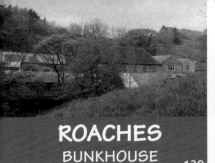

ROACHES
BUNKHOUSE

130

The Roaches Bunkhouse is at the foot of The Roaches gritstone edge in the Peak District. The area has some of the best climbing in the country plus walks & cycling in stunning scenery.

The communal area has tables & chairs, log fire, DVDs & board games. Self-catering facilities are available in a small kitchen. Outside BBQ area. On site parking. Walking distance of Ye Old Rock Inn & the Roaches Tearooms. 3 miles to the bustling market town of Leek.

DETAILS
- **Open** - All year.
- **Beds** - 42: 9x4, 3x2
- **Price/night** - From £12 pp. Sole Use from £500.

CONTACT: Emma Baines
Tel: 01538 300308
info@roachesbunkhouse.com
www.roachesbunkhouse.com
Upper Hulme Mill, Roach Road, Upper Hulme, Nr Leek, Staffordshire, ST13 8TY

ROYAL OAK
BUNKBARN

131

A refurbished stone barn next to an award winning Peak District country pub, The Royal Oak Bunkbarn is perfectly situated with direct access onto the High Peak and Tissington Trails (disused railways for easy off-road cycling). The area is also very popular with climbers and walkers with limestone gorges and stone circles to explore. The bunkbarn offers comfortable, clean bunk bed style rooms. The five separate bunk rooms are all heated and lockable. Campsite and holiday cottages also available.

DETAILS

- **Open** - All year. All day.
- **Beds** - 34: 3x8, 1x6, 1x4
- **Price/night** - April to Sept £17pppn, Oct to March £15pppn.

CONTACT: The Royal Oak
Tel: 01298 83288
hello@peakpub.co.uk
www.peakpub.co.uk
The Royal Oak, Hurdlow, Nr Buxton,
SK17 9QJ

THE RECKONING
HOUSE
132

Renovated to a high standard including double glazing and insulation, the Reckoning House is situated 3 miles from Bakewell. It is on the edge of the Lathkill Dale National Nature Reserve, full of interesting flora and fauna as well as outstanding geological features. Horse riding, fishing, golf and cycle hire are available locally. Local walks include the Limestone Way. Facilities include: cooking area, 4 calor gas rings (gas supplied), hot water for washing up & showers, storage heaters in all rooms.

DETAILS

- **Open** - All year. By arrangement.
- **Beds** - 12: 2x6 bunk rooms.
- **Price/night** - £15 per person. Sole use £95 per night.

CONTACT: Rachel Rhodes
Tel: 01629 812416 or 07540 839233
mandalecampsite@yahoo.co.uk
www.mandalecampsite.co.uk
Mandale Farm, Haddon Grove,
Bakewell, Derbyshire, DE45 1JF

THORNBRIDGE
OUTDOORS

133

Thornbridge Outdoors offers excellent flexible group accommodation. With its superb location in the heart of the Peak District you have access to wonderful countryside, quaint villages, stately homes, and the traffic free Monsal Trail, popular with walkers and cyclists.

        **GROUPS ONLY**

DETAILS

■ **Open** - All year. All day. Reception Mon-Fri 9am-5pm

■ **Beds** - Whole site: 90 + camping. Lodge 38: 4x5, 4x3, 1x6. Farm House 38: 2x8, 2x6, 1x5, 1x3, 1x2. Woodlands 10: 1x5, 1x4, 1x1. Woodlands Cottage 4: 2x2. Teepees 45: 9x4/5. Plus camping.

■ **Price/night** - Weekend breaks from £252 (Woodlands Cottage), £396 (Woodlands), £1,164 (Farm House), and £1,464 (Lodge).

CONTACT: Reception Team
Tel: 01629 640491
info@thornbridgeoutdoors.co.uk
www.thornbridgeoutdoors.co.uk
Great Longstone, Bakewell, DE45 1NY

BRETTON
HOSTEL

Bretton Hostel, near historic Eyam in the heart of the Peak District, feels remote surrounded by fields on Bretton Edge. With glorious far-reaching views across the Dark and White Peak and excellent walks and cycle rides from the door. Sleeps 17, bedding provided, kitchen, sitting room, wood burner, studio.

DETAILS

- **Open** - Groups (sole use): All year. Individuals: Apr-Oct (Mon-Thu). Arrive from 4pm, depart by 11am.
- **Beds** - 17: 1x8, 1x6, 1x3
- **Price/night** - Sole use from £252 per night (min 2 nights stay). More for large groups and weekends. Individuals: £25 one night, £21 two or more nights. Sorry, sole use bookings only at weekends.

CONTACT: Clare Palmer
Tel: 07792 385134
bookings@brettonhostel.co.uk
brettonhostel.co.uk
Bretton, near Eyam, Hope Valley,
Derbyshire S32 5QD

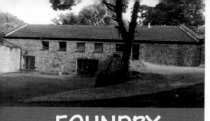

FOUNDRY
ADVENTURE CENTRE 135

With all of the Peak District National Park within easy access, the centre is an ideal location for activities and tourism and it welcomes a wide range of groups. 31 or 52 bed configurations can be booked.

The spacious centre includes; a large lounge with library, TV and wood burning stove, well equipped kitchens & dining areas. An extensive network of paths give access to the countryside. Adventure activities available, great for team building & courses.

   **GROUPS ONLY**

DETAILS

- **Open** - All year. All day.
- **Beds** - 52 or 31 in 9 bedrooms
- **Price/night** - 31 beds from £790 per night, 52 beds from £1120 per night.

CONTACT: Tim Gould
Tel: 07786 332702
tim@foundrymountain.co.uk
foundryadventurecentre.co.uk
The Old Playhouse, Great Hucklow,
Derbyshire, SK17 8RF

PINDALE
OUTDOOR CENTRE
136

A mile from Castleton in the Peak District, Pindale Farm offers a range of accommodation: B&B in the farmhouse. The Barn has 6 self-catering units. The Engine House is a self-catering unit & The Powder House is a small camping barn. Plus a campsite. Perfect for many outdoor activities. Instruction is available.

DETAILS

■ **Open** - All year (camping March-October). 24 hours.

■ **Beds** - 64: Farmhouse: 4. Engine House: 8. Powder House: 4. The Barn: 6x8 -10. Plus camping.

■ **Price/night** - Camping £8.50pp (hook up £4). Barns £18pp + £1 electric tokens. Enquire for B&B. Discount of £0.50pppn for DofE campers.

CONTACT: Alan Medhurst
Tel: 01433 620111
info@pindalefarm.co.uk
www.pindalefarm.co.uk
Pindale Road, Hope, Hope Valley,
Derbyshire, S33 6RN

ST MICHAELS
CENTRE

St Michael's Centre, located in the village of Hathersage, provides high quality family friendly group accommodation, surrounded by the beautiful countryside of the Peak District National Park. The centre has comfortable dormitory style accommodation with bunk beds. There is a lovely central hall which provides a fantastic communal kitchen, dining and lounge area for enjoyable shared living. Attached cottage also available, separately or for larger groups.

 **GROUPS ONLY**

DETAILS

■ **Open** - All year. Office open Monday to Friday 8.30 am - 4pm
■ **Beds** - 38: 2x2, 1x4, 2x6, 1x8, 1x10. Plus 4/6 in attached cottage.
■ **Price/night** - Minimum 20 beds, from £470 per night, min stay: 2 nights.

CONTACT: Centre office
Tel: 01433 650309
stmichaels@nottscc.gov.uk
www.nottinghamshire.gov.uk
Main Road, Hathersage, S32 1BB

THORPE FARM
BUNKHOUSES

Close to Hathersage and 2 miles west of Stanage Edge, the bunkhouses are on a family-run dairy farm. Popular areas for climbing, walking from meadows to moorland with fantastic views & mountain biking. Each bunkhouse is heated and has a living room, kitchen, bathrooms with toilets, showers and washbasins. Sleep in dorms with bunks or the Hayloft has mattresses on the gallery floor. Camping is available. Secure bike storage and free parking.

DETAILS

- **Open** - All year. No restrictions.
- **Beds** - Old Shippon 32: 2x12, 2x4. Old Stables 14 1x8, 1x6. Pondside 14: 1x8, 1x6. Byre 14: 1x6, 1x4. Living Room 4.
- **Price/night** - See own website.

CONTACT: Jane Marsden
Tel: 01433 650659
jane@hope-valley.co.uk
www.thorpe-bunk.co.uk
Thorpe Farm, Hathersage, Peak District,
Via Sheffield, S32 1BQ

HOMESTEAD
AND CHEESEHOUSE

In the heart of Bamford these two bunkhouses are on a small farm just 3 miles from the iconic Stanage Edge. The Derwent Dams are close by. Perfectly located for visiting Castleton, Chatsworth House & Hathersage. Both bunkhouses are centrally heated have hot showers and well equipped kitchens. Sheets & pillows are provided (BYO sleeping bags). Book separately or together. Sorry, no dogs.

DETAILS
- **Open** - All year. Check in after 4pm. Check out by 11am.
- **Beds** - Homestead 22: 1x10, 2x6. Cheesehouse 4: 1x4
- **Price/night** - From £15 pp. Sole use: Homestead £210, Cheesehouse £45. Min 2 nights for Homestead at weekends. Phone for a quote for single night.

CONTACT: Helena Platts
Tel: 01433 651298
The Farm, Bamford, Hope Valley,
S33 0BL

DALEHEAD
BUNKHOUSE

Dalehead Bunkhouse is on a working hill farm at the remote head of Edale Valley. Providing basic but comfortable accommodation heated by log burner & infrared radiant heat. There is a kitchen with fridge/freezer, a lounge, dining room and plenty of parking. Please bring sleeping bags, pillows and towels.

Edale is popular with walkers, climbers, mountain bikers, hang-gliders or for enjoying the magnificent scenery.

DETAILS

- **Open** - All year. All day.
- **Beds** - 20: 1x6, 1x8, 1x6
- **Price/night** - Mon-Wed £120 per night. Thur-Sun £330. Min 2 nights Fri-Sun, 3 bank holidays. Dogs £15 per dog per stay.

CONTACT: National Trust Holidays
Tel: 03443 351296
bunkhouses@nationaltrust.org.uk
www.nationaltrust.org.uk/holidays
Dalehead Bunkhouse, Upper Booth,
Edale, Hope Valley, S33 7ZJ

EDALE BARN
COTEFIELD FARM
141a

UPPER BOOTH
CAMPING BARN
141b

Overlooking Mam Tor, at the start of the Pennine Way, Edale Barn is a traditional camping barn, a stone tent with a wooden sleeping platform. Close to Kinder Scout, Jacobs Ladder, Kinder Downfall & Hollins Cross. Adjoining the barn, but with external access, is a cooking area with a mains water tap and a chemical toilet. There is no heating or electricity. BYO sleeping mats/bags, cooking equipment and torches. Pubs serving meals are as easy walk away.

Next to a small campsite alongside Crowden Clough in the Peak District. Hire the simple barn and additional pitches on the campsite. There is space for cooking (BYO equipment and beds) and tables for eating. Toilets, sinks & showers are shared with the campsite. On a working hill-farm, the Pennine Way passes through the farmyard and there is great mountain biking locally.

DETAILS

DETAILS

- **Open** - All year. Arrive after 4pm and depart before 10am.
- **Beds** - 8 on a raised wooden platform
- **Price/night** - £8.50 per person. £68 sole use per night.

- **Open** - March-November. Arrival between 3pm and 9pm. Departure before 10am. Not suitable for late night parties.
- **Beds** - 12 sleeping spaces & camping.
- **Price/night** - Sole use (up to 12 persons) from £90 per night plus vehicles. Individuals from £10 per person per night.

CONTACT: Rachael Gee
Tel: 01433 651901 or 07739 828383
reg1102@hotmail.com
www.fb.com/cotefieldfarmcottages
Cotefield Farm Olllerbrook Edale Hope Valley Derbyshire S33 7ZG

CONTACT: Robert, Sarah or Alice
Tel: 01433 670250
mail@helliwell.info
www.upperboothcamping.co.uk
Upper Booth Farm, Edale, Hope Valley, Derbyshire, S33 7ZJ

OLLERBROOK
FARM BUNKHOUSES

Close to the start of the Pennine Way with easy access to Kinder Scout and the village of Edale via a network of footpaths from the doorstep. Castleton, Buxton, Bakewell and Chatsworth House are all within 40 minutes' drive. There are 2 bunkhouses each with a fully equipped kitchen and available for sole use by groups. Bring your own sleeping bags.

       GROUPS ONLY

DETAILS

- **Open** - All year. All day. Arrive after 4pm depart before 10.30am.
- **Beds** - Nab View 18: 3x6, Stables Bunkhouse 16: 4x4
- **Price/night** - Nab View: £330. The Stables: midweek £200, weekends £230. Enquire for longer stays and prices for room or bed. Minimum of two night stay.

CONTACT: Sheila
Tel: 01433 670235
ollerbrookfarm@gmail.com
www.ollerbrookfarm.co.uk
Ollerbrook Booth, Edale, Hope Valley,
Derbyshire, S33 7ZG

JOHN HUNT
BASE

143

The John Hunt Base is situated in the High Peak on the site of Hagg Farm (see page 144)

The base offers comfortable, family friendly accommodation ideal for sightseeing, hill walking, trail running and biking as well as quieter pursuits such as photography. There is a picnic area, wildlife garden with fire pit and a playing field with climbing boulder. Activities can be arranged including climbing, stream scrambling, caving & on-site high ropes.

       GROUPS ONLY

DETAILS

- **Open** - All year. Office, Mon-Thur 8.30am- 4.30pm, Fri 8.30-3.30pm
- **Beds** - 18: 1x8, 1x6, 2x2
- **Price/night** - £300 min 2 nights. Instruction (12 people) from £300 per day.

CONTACT:
Tel: 01433 651594
haggfarm@nottscc.gov.uk
www.nottinghamshire.gov.uk/haggfarm
Hagg Farm OEC, Snake Rd, Bamford,
Hope Valley, S33 0BJ

HAGG FARM
OUTDOOR CENTRE
144

Situated in the Peak District's Woodlands Valley, Hagg Farm offers comfortable accommodation for up to 44 people with an additional 18 beds in the John Hunt Base next door (see page 143). Part of Nottinghamshire C.C's Environmental & Outdoor Education Service, Hagg Farm is available for private hire by groups, families, clubs & charitable organisations. It can be booked on a self-catering or catered basis.

       GROUPS ONLY

DETAILS
- **Open** - All year. Office: Mon-Thurs 8:30am-4.30pm Fri 8:30am-4pm
- **Beds** - 44: 4x8, 2x4, 2x2
- **Price/night** - £24pp: min charge for 25 people, min 2 night stay. Outdoor activity instruction for 12 from £300 per day.

CONTACT: Kirsty Weatherall
Tel: 01433 651594
haggfarm@nottscc.gov.uk
www.nottinghamshire.gov.uk/haggfarm
Hagg Farm OEC, Snake Rd, Bamford,
Hope Valley, S33 0BJ

Nottinghamshire County Council

LOCKERBROOK FARM
OUTDOOR CENTRE
145

Lockerbrook Farm provides remote accommodation for groups of 15 to 38 people with with stunning views across Snakes Pass to the Peak District Edges.

Sleeping is in three large dorms and five smaller rooms. There is a large kitchen and dining area, ideal for groups to self cater and an enormous activity room with lounge area and a splendid wood burning stove. Catering can be provided.

     **GROUPS ONLY**

DETAILS
- **Open** - All year
- **Beds** - 38: 5x2,1x6,1x10,1x12
- **Price/night** - 2 night weekend from £880. Single night midweek from £472, 2 night stay midweek from £880. Discounts for youth and school groups.

CONTACT: Jo Holliday or Jason Lock
Tel: 01433 651412
lockerbrook@woodcraft.org.uk
lockerbrook.org.uk
Snake Pass, Bamford, Hope Valley,
Derbyshire, S33 0BJ

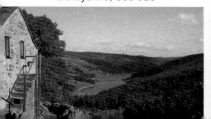

BRADWELL
WAR MEMORIAL HALL
146a

BOARSHURST CENTRE
SADDLEWORTH
146b

Bradwell War Memorial Hall is in the pretty village of Bradwell in the heart of the Peak District. This community run hall offers low cost self-catering accommodation to groups of 6-42.

An ideal base for walkers, bikers, DofE students or climbers who wish to explore this popular area. There are no beds so BYO sleeping mat and bedding. The rooms are centrally heated, there's a well equipped kitchen & hot showers.

The Boarshurst Centre is situated on the north western edge of the Peak District yet with easy road and rail links to Manchester (12 miles away). With 32 beds across 2 dorms and 2 leaders rooms the centre provides well appointed self catering accommodation for affiliated child, youth and adult groups from registered charities and organisations who seek to practice outdoor pursuits. BYO sheets and sleeping bags

DETAILS

- **Open** - Weekends and school holidays only.
- **Beds** - 42: 1x30, 1x6, 1x4/6
- **Price/night** - £150 per night, weekends and school holidays only.

DETAILS

- **Open** - All year. Check in 12 noon or earlier by arrangement.
- **Beds** - 32: 2x12, 2x4
- **Price/night** - Sole use only. Adults £20pp, 12-16yrs £15, under 12s £10. Min group size 20.

CONTACT: Laura Mannion
Tel: 07772 297738
bradwellwarmemorial@gmail.com
Netherside, Bradwell, Hope Valley, Derbyshire S33 9HJ

CONTACT: Pam Byrne
Tel: 01457 820149
theboarshurstcentre@gmail.com
www.boarshurstcentre.org
3 Boarshurst Lane, Greenfield, Oldham OL3 7EA

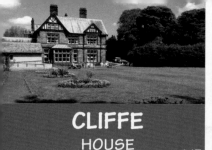

CLIFFE
HOUSE

Cliffe House is set in 14 acres of woodland in rural West Yorkshire, just 7 miles from the Peak District. A centre for outdoor learning and conferences, ideal for schools and businesses, it is also available as a whole house booking to groups of families and friends. There are 10 bed rooms sleeping up to 72 people and three bright communal areas with seating for 40 people in each.

       GROUPS ONLY

DETAILS

- **Open** - All year. All day access.
- **Beds** - 72: in 10 bedrooms
- **Price/night** - Sole use of House from £575. Breakfast buffet £7pp. School groups fully catered with activities from £80pp, £135 for 2 nights (minimum 30 people). Winter discounts.

CONTACT: The Team
Tel: 01484 225083 option 3
enquiries.cliffehouse@kirklees.gov.uk
www.kirklees.gov.uk
140 Lane Head Road, Shepley, West Yorkshire, HD8 8DB

EMBASSIE
BACKPACKERS
148a

STABLESIDE
YORK
148b

The Embassie is a majestic terraced house in an unspoilt Georgian square. Until 1986 it was the Consulate of Venezuela! Only 15 minutes' walk from the centre of Liverpool, known for its nightlife, it's in the perfect position. Recently refurbished, there are new kitchen facilities, a brand new shower suite and an all new games room & relax area with Sky Sports and HD television. The hostel is clean, safe and staffed 24 hours. Bedding is provided (including sheets) and free coffee, tea, toast and jam are available 24 hours.

Stableside, a quiet & welcoming 4* hostel situated right on the historic Knavesmire, is the perfect location for enjoying a break in the beautiful city of York. Guests can take advantage of the varied room options catering for the single traveller and larger groups. Free parking, free WiFi and a fabulous Yorkshire welcome. Meals can be provided for groups. On the NCN Route 65 for easy access to the city centre.

DETAILS
- **Open** - All year. All day.
- **Beds** - 50
- **Price/night** - £19 (Sunday to Thursday), £25 Friday, £32 Saturday

DETAILS
- **Open** - All year (except during race meetings). All day.
- **Beds** - 100: 2x6, 21x4, 8 x triple, 1 x twin, 11 x single.
- **Price/night** - B&B twin room £90 inc towels. Enquire for group rates.

CONTACT: Kevin
Tel: 0151 707 1089
embassie@gmail.com
www.embassie.com
1 Falkner Square, Liverpool, L8 7NU

CONTACT: Fay
Tel: 01904 709174
fay.waudby@yorkracecourse.co.uk
www.stablesideyork.co.uk
Stableside, York Racing Stables, York, YO24 1QG

ASTOR YORK
HOSTEL

Astor York is set in a beautiful Grade II listed building just minutes' walk to the historic centre!

With a huge cosy lounge & dining areas, free WiFi throughout the building and every room en suite, Astor York is the perfect base for exploring the incredible historic centre of York. There is also a bar on the property if you fancy a drink with friends, or to meet fellow travellers, and a kitchen where you can cook your own food if you are on a budget!

DETAILS

- **Open** - All year
- **Beds** - 93: 1x1, 1x twin, 2x dbl. 9x4, 2x6, 1x8, 1x12, 1x18
- **Price/night** - Dorm beds from £17pp. Private double/twin from £58.

CONTACT: Eric
Tel: 01904 653 786
eric@astorhostels.com
astorhostels.com/hostels/york
124 Holgate Road, York, YO24 4BB

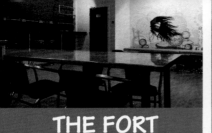

THE FORT
BOUTIQUE HOSTEL
150a

SCARBOROUGH
YOUTH HOSTEL
150b

Step outside The Fort Boutique Hostel into an area of York steeped in history and surrounded by lively cafés, bars and restaurants. The hostel has comfortable, stylish accommodation with flat screen TVs and WiFi. Complimentary hot drinks are available. And if you are feeling hungry, meals are available locally as The Fort is situated above Kennedy's Bar and Restaurant, a popular, independently owned venue.

So, relax, order a drink and enjoy this vibrant, unique spot, smack bang in the heart of York.

For a fun filled, seaside break Scarborough is unbeatable: two safe, sandy beaches, penny arcades, pirate ship, three surf schools and the new Alpamare Waterpark. Once a 17th century water mill on a quiet riverside just outside the town, Scarborough Youth Hostel is also a perfect base for exploring the coast and country of the North York Moors and Wolds with miles of paths, tracks and quiet lanes for walkers and cyclists.

DETAILS

■ **Open** - Seasonal. 7.30-10am & 5-10pm.
■ **Beds** - 46: 5x6, 4x4.
■ **Price/night** - Beds from £16, rooms from £55, discounts for YHA members

DETAILS

■ **Open** - All year. 24hrs.
■ **Beds** - 60: 5x2 4x8 3x6
■ **Price/night** - From £18 per person

CONTACT: Fiona Helme
Tel: 01904 639573
info@thefortyork.co.uk
www.thefortyork.co.uk
1 Little Stonegate, York, YO1 8AX

CONTACT: Robert Fletcher
Tel: 01723 361176
scarboroughhostel@gmail.com
www.scarboroughhostel.com
The White House, Burniston Road,
Scarborough, YO13 0DA

BANK HOUSE
FARM HOSTEL
151

Luxury bunkbarn, camping barn and B&B on an organic farm in beautiful Glaisdale Dale. Stunning views of the North York Moors and just 1 mile from the Coast to Coast route. The newly converted bunkbarn is warm & well appointed with one dorm of mostly single beds. The camping barn provides simple, single-night shelter for walkers and cyclists.

DETAILS

- **Open** - All year. Phone calls 9am-9pm
- **Beds** - Bunkbarn: 1x11 (9 singles 1 bunk) Camping barn: 8: 2x4
- **Price/night** - Bunkbarn: W/ends £500 (2 nights), Bank Hols £600 (3 nights). Saturday £400. Midweek from £25pppn. Deals for longer stays. Camping Barn: £12pp. Farmhouse B&B: £40.

CONTACT: Chris or Emma Padmore
Tel: 01947 897297
info@bankhousefarmhostel.co.uk
www.bankhousefarmhostel.co.uk
Bank House Farm, Glaisdale, Whitby
YO21 2QA

BRANSDALE MILL
BUNKHOUSE
152

Bransdale Mill is an eighteenth century Grade II listed water mill, converted by the National Trust to provide comfortable bunkhouse accommodation for 12.

It is full of historic character with flag-stone floors, wooden beams and a log burner. Situated at the head of an unspoiled and hidden valley in the North York Moors, 3 miles from the Coast to Coast walk. With no WiFi or phone signal, Bransdale Mill is an ideal base to get away from it all.

      **GROUPS ONLY**

DETAILS
- **Open** - All year. All day
- **Beds** - 12: 2x6
- **Price/night** - From £300 for two nights sole use. (Min booking 2 nights).

CONTACT: National Trust Holidays
Tel: 03443 351296
bunkhouses@nationaltrust.org.uk
www.nationaltrust.org.uk/holidays
Bransdale Mill, Bransdale, Fadmoor,
York YO62 7JL

COTE GHYLL
MILL
153

Situated in a beautiful secluded valley in the NY Moors National Park, this refurbished mill with en suite rooms, is perfect for those wishing to explore the Yorkshire moors, dales & coast. You can book the whole Mill, a room or a bed. Great for educational groups, families, outdoor clubs and gatherings of friends. Group activities and catering available. Next to Cod Beck reservoir, Cleveland Way, Coast to Coast & Lyke Wake Walk.

        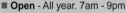

DETAILS
- **Open** - All year. 7am - 9pm
- **Beds** - 71: Mill 61: 4x2, 6x4, 4x6 + 5 rollout beds. Annex: 10
- **Price/night** - Adults from £26. U18's from £20.80. Family rooms from £50. Enquire for groups & sole use.

CONTACT: Reception
Tel: 01609 883425
mill@coteghyll.com
www.coteghyll.com
Osmotherley, Northallerton, North
Yorkshire, DL6 3AH

BROMPTON ON SWALE
BUNKBARN
154a

154b
WEST END
OUTDOOR CENTRE

Located on a small working farm, just 3 miles east of Richmond, Yorkshire. Brompton on Swale Bunkbarn offers a welcome break from walking or cycling the Coast to Coast. A pot of tea for weary walkers upon arrival and safe storage for bikes makes this bunkhouse especially welcoming. Close to the Yorkshire Dales, Swaledale, Wensleydale, Easby Abbey, Richmond Castle & Ellerton Lakes. Dogs are welcome to stay but must be kept on a lead around the yard as there are ducks, hens and geese.

Set amidst stunning landscape overlooking Thruscross Reservoir on the edge of the Yorkshire Dales National Park, this self-catering centre offers excellent facilities in bunkrooms plus an en suite leaders' room. Well equipped kitchen, dining, lounge & shower/toilet areas. Ideal for team building, youth groups & family parties. 12 miles from Harrogate & Skipton. No stag or hen groups.

DETAILS

- **Open** - All year. All day
- **Beds** - 12: 3x4
- **Price/night** - £12pp. £144 sole use. Sleeping bag hire £1

DETAILS

- **Open** - All year. Flexible.
- **Beds** - 30: 4x2, 3x4, 1x6, 1x4 en suite
- **Price/night** - Sole use: Fri+Sat £385, Fri+Sat+BH £1100. Midweek £240 (min 2 nights). 4 nights midweek: £800, 7 nights £1300. 1 night midweek £300. £5 per dog

CONTACT: Chris Wilkin
Tel: 01748 818326
chris01748@gmail.com
www.facebook.com/Bromptononswalebunkbarn
24 Richmond Road, Richmond, North Yorkshire, DL10 7HE

CONTACT: Hedley or Margaret Verity
Tel: 01943 880207
info@westendoutdoorcentre.co.uk
www.westendoutdoorcentre.co.uk
West End, Summerbridge, Harrogate, HG3 4BA

TRAWDEN
CAMPING BARN
155a

DOWNHAM
CAMPING BARN
155b

Trawden Camping Barn is a listed stone barn on Middle Beardshaw Farm. Surrounded by stunning landscape, the nearby village of Wycoller has been much used by film crews. The barn is large & open with an ancient timbered roof. The barn sleeps 37: 7 beds/bunks & 30 mattresses (BYO sleeping bags) with lots of communal space, a table tennis & pool table and a well equipped kitchen (in a separate building just 15m away). Pub & café just a short walk.

With unrivalled views of Pendle Hill, Downham Camping Barn is a short walk from Downham village pubs & cafes.

Popular with walkers, cyclists & DofE groups the recently refurbished barn sleeps 12 (BYO camp beds or roll mats). There's a basic kitchen, sitting area, hot shower & WC. Photovoltaic cells provide power for limited LED lighting (but not for phone charging) and there is a wood-burning stove with fuel available to purchase. Outside there is a gas BBQ & fire pit and space for tents.

DETAILS
- **Open** - All year. Warm clothes and sleeping bags required in winter
- **Beds** - 37 (7 beds + 30 mattresses)
- **Price/night** - £15pp plus £10 per night per group for electricity. Visitors can bring their own fuel for the fire or buy it on-site.

DETAILS
- **Open** - All year.
- **Beds** - 12: 1x12
- **Price/night** - £12 pp.

CONTACT: Ursula
Tel: 01282 865257
ursula78beardshaw@gmail.com
Middle Beardshaw Head Farm, Burnley Road, Trawden Lancashire, BB8 8PP

CONTACT: Bookings Secretary
Tel: 01200 441667
info@downhamvillage.org.uk
www.downhamvillage.org.uk
Twiston Lane, Downham, Clitheroe, Lancs. BB7 4DF

EARBY
HOSTEL

Cosy, historic hostel with large kitchen & dining room which can seat all 21 people in one room. Lounge with log burner. Secure cycle storage for 20 bikes. Large wildlife garden with BBQ. Private parking for 6 cars.

Great local pub. Medium sized Coop supermarket open 7 days 6am to 10pm. Food available with prior request. Good public transport links.

DETAILS

- **Open** - All year.
- **Beds** - 26: Hostel 21: 1x2, 2x6, 1x7. Cottage 5: 1xdbl, 1x3
- **Price/night** - £20pp, or £400 for exclusive use of the whole hostel. Adjoining family cottage (sleeps 5) £65.

CONTACT: Matt
Tel: 01282 842349 or 07791 903454
matt@earbyhostel.co.uk
earbyhostel.co.uk
9-11 Birch Hall Lane, Earby, Lancashire, BB18 6JX

HEBDEN BRIDGE
HOSTEL
157

Expect a warm welcome at Hebden Bridge Hostel. Comfy and welcoming, nestled into woodland, it is only a short walk from the town centre and less than 500m from the Hebden Bridge Loop on the Pennine Way.

A perfect base for hiking, sight-seeing, relaxing or experiencing Hebden Bridge's vibrant cafés, music, arts and culture.

DETAILS
- **Open** - Easter to end of October. Sole use all year. Arrive 5-8pm, leave by 10am.
- **Beds** - 33 : 6x4 (or 2), 1x3 (or 2), 1x6
- **Price/night** - Bunkroom £15pp. Dorm £20pp. Twin £55. Double £60. Double+1 £75. Private 4-bed room £75. Midweek single £35. Sole use available.

CONTACT: Em
Tel: 01422 843183
mama@hebdenbridgehostel.co.uk
www.hebdenbridgehostel.co.uk
The Birchcliffe Centre, Hebden Bridge,
W Yorks, HX7 8DG

AIRTON BARN

158a

GRASSINGTON
BUNKBARN

158b

A friendly welcome awaits you at Airton Barn. Next to the 17th century Friends Meeting House, Airton Barn is a simple bunkhouse sleeping up to 18 people over two floors, with storage space for 5 bicycles. On popular walking & cycling routes & surrounded by some of Yorkshire's finest tourist destinations, the Barn is perfect for walkers, cyclists & small group getaways.

With spectacular views of Wharfedale, Grassington Bunkbarn offers comfortable accommodation for individuals and groups. Featuring a well equipped kitchen and a lounge/games area with Freeview TV, WiFi, good mobile signal & a BBQ area. Walking, cycling, climbing, fishing, horse riding, archaeology, bird watching, geology, botany & golf nearby. There's something for everyone.

DETAILS

■ **Open** - All year. Volunteer warden resident on site.
■ **Beds** - 18: 6 bunks + 6 mattresses + 6 air beds. Overflow camping for 2 tents.
■ **Price/night** - £18pp, reducing for larger groups. Call to discuss. £5 to hire bedlinen & towel if needed.

CONTACT: Simon Watkins, Friend in Residence
Tel: 01729 830263
airtonbarn.org.uk
The Nook, Airton, Skipton, North Yorkshire, BD23 4AE

DETAILS

■ **Open** - All year. Reception 9am - 5pm Mon - Fri, Sat 10am - 2pm.
■ **Beds** - 34: 2x12, 1x6, 1x4
■ **Price/night** - Sole use: W/E: £1100 (2 ngts). BH: £1350 (3 ngts). Midweek: £410pn. 4 ngts: £1250. 7 ngts: from £2150. Bed £26 (call for availability).

CONTACT: Paul, Mark or Janet Kent
Tel: 01756 753882
enquiries@grassingtonbunkbarn.co.uk
www.grassingtonbunkbarn.co.uk
Spring Croft, Moor Lane, Grassington, BD23 5BD

NIDDERDALE
BUNKHOUSE

159

Exclusive hire in the stunning Nidderdale Valley overlooking Gouthwaite reservoir. The bunkhouse has a well equipped, open plan kitchen, beautiful dining & seating areas with great views. The Nidderdale Way goes right past the house. The Yorke Arms, Michelin star restaurant, is nearby. The award winning village of Pateley Bridge has pubs, cafés and festivities throughout the year. Perfect for walkers and wildlife lovers or to explore Yorkshire. Up to 2 dogs welcome by arrangement.

    GROUPS ONLY

DETAILS

- **Open** - All year. All day.
- **Beds** - 20: 1x8, 3x4
- **Price/night** - From just £18 per person. Exclusive group hire

CONTACT: Matt or Bev
Tel: 07597 645254
nidderdalebunkhouse@gmail.com
www.nidderdalebunkhouse.com
Ramsgill, Harrogate, North Yorkshire
HG3 5RH

SKIRFARE
BARN

Skirfare Barn, with its stunning backdrop of Upper Wharfedale & Littondale, nestles in the Yorkshire Dales with the climbers' challenge, Kilnsey Crag, on the doorstep. The area is famous for walking & cycling with many footpaths, including the Dales Way, close by. At nearby Kilnsey you can book day fishing & food at The Kilnsey Park, or bar snacks at The Tennant Arms Hotel. Pony & Llama trekking & many other activities are also nearby. The barn provides warm, comfortable accommodation for walking, cycling, friends or family groups.

🛆 🅿 ◇ ▥ ⌂ ▦ ⊷ ((•)) 🐕 **GROUPS ONLY**

DETAILS

- **Open** - All year.
- **Beds** - 20: 2x2 (twin), 2x4, 1x8.
- **Price/night** - From £16 per person.

CONTACT:
Tel: 01756 636350
info@skirfarebarn.com
www.skirfarebarn.com
Kettlewell Rd, Kilnsey, North Yorkshire, BD23 5PT

KETTLEWELL
HOSTEL

The Rose Award winning Kettlewell Hostel is a stylish Independent Youth Hostel in the heart of the Yorkshire Dales. Serving hearty, great value homemade meals & local beer in our large dining room. There's a cosy lounge with woodburner, a lovely garden, self-catering kitchen & big bike shed! Sleeps up to 42 in 11 bedrooms. Great walking and cycling routes on the doorstep.

DETAILS

■ **Open** - All year. Reception 8-10.30am, 4-10pm.

■ **Beds** - 42: 1 x twin, 1 x double, 4x3, 2x4, 2x6, 1x5/6

■ **Price/night** - Beds from £25, private rooms for 2 from £59. Sole use from £400/night.

CONTACT: Saul & Floss Ward
Tel: 01756 760232
saulward@hotmail.com
www.yha.org.uk/hostel/kettlewell
Whernside House, Kettlewell, Skipton,
North Yorkshire, BD23 5QU

MALHAM TARN
BOTHIES
162

On the National Trust Malham Tarn Estate in North Yorkshire, Ragged Robin Bothy & Meadowsweet Bothy each sleep 6 people on bunk bed platforms. Like camping but without the tent, you need to bring mats, sleeping bags and cooking equipment. There is one external toilet, cold water and no heating or lighting.

A perfect location for those who want to escape technology, enjoy dark skies or walk the Pennine Way.

DETAILS
- **Open** - 1 April to 31 October
- **Beds** - 12: Ragged Robin Bothy 6:1x6, Meadowsweet Bothy 6:1x6
- **Price/night** - £30 per bothy in low season, £40 in high season.

CONTACT: National Trust Holidays
Tel: 03443 351296
bunkhouses@nationaltrust.org.uk
www.nationaltrust.org.uk/holidays
Malham Tarn Estate, Waterhouses, Settle, North Yorkshire, BD24 9PT

TOWN HEAD
BARN

163

Town Head Barn is a converted barn, located in Upper Wharfedale, in the small village of Buckden. The accommodation sleeps 13 in 4 rooms including a single leader's room with en suite facilities.

Close (just 3.5 miles) to the village of Kettlewell with pubs and shops and with easy access to Buckden Pike which at 702m high is just waiting to be climbed. This is the perfect location for groups or families wanting to get away from it all in the Yorkshire Dales National Park.

DETAILS

- **Open** - All year. All day
- **Beds** - 13: 3x4,1x1
- **Price/night** - From £338 for two nights sole use. (Min booking 2 nights).

CONTACT: National Trust Holidays
Tel: 03443 351296
bunkhouses@nationaltrust.org.uk
www.nationaltrust.org.uk/holidays
Buckden, Skipton, North Yorkshire,
BD23 5JA

THE DALESBRIDGE

In the Three Peaks area of the Yorkshire Dales, The Dalesbridge has 8 stylish B&B rooms, 8 cabins with bunks, 4 glamping pods & over 100 camping pitches. There's a cosy bar with log burner & wood fired pizzas at weekends. Two large conference rooms, catering services & a unique event tent makes Dalesbridge ideal for many events and conferences. The stunning local area is perfect for walking, caving & climbing.

DETAILS

- **Open** - All year
- **Beds** - 48: Cabins: 4x4, 4x6. Pods: 4x2. B&B: 8x2. Camping: 100+ pitches, 40+ hook ups.
- **Price/night** - From: 4 bed cabin £55, 6 bed cabin £80. Pods £40. B&B £85. Camping £15.

CONTACT: Aimee & Ross
Tel: 01524 251021
info@dalesbridge.co.uk
www.dalesbridge.co.uk
Austwick, Nr Settle, LA2 8AZ

DALE HOUSE
BARN

Dale House Barn is in the heart of Gisburn Forest in the Forest of Bowland AONB. Sympathetically restored it offers simple, practical accommodation for groups of 4-14. Mattresses provided, BYO bedding. Well equipped kitchen. Free WiFi . Close to the Three Peaks, Pendle Hill, Malham Tarn & the Yorkshire Dales. Ideal for walking, climbing, fishing, cycling, family gatherings and activity groups. Meals available. B&B in the adjoining farmhouse.

DETAILS

- **Open** - All year.
- **Beds** - 14: 1x14
- **Price/night** - £18pp (min 4 people). W/ ends and Bank Hols, sole use only; £185. (2 nights min stay 31 Mar-1st Oct.

CONTACT: Dominique Ashford
Tel: 01200 411095 or 07714 092089
ashforddominique1@mac.com
www.dalehousebarn.co.uk
Dalehead Farm, Dalehead, Slaidburn, Clitheroe, Lancashire, BB7 4TS

HORNBY LAITHE
BUNKHOUSE BARN
166a

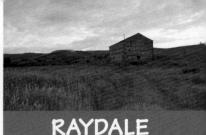

RAYDALE
BARN
166b

Simple, comfortable accommodation in the Yorkshire Dales National Park, Hornby Laith Bunkhouse Barn occupies a secluded position within easy walking distance of the pretty village of Stainforth and the market town of Settle. It is within easy access of a wide variety of routes for walkers and climbers. Sleeping up to 5O, there is a separate barn containing a recreational area, extra camping and space for a marquee for events/ weddings & ample parking. There's a self-catering kitchen and full catering can be organised by arrangement.

Raydale Barn is an off-grid camping barn nr Lake Semerwater in the Yorkshire Dales National Park. Matresses for 16 inside plus camping outside in the barn's own field.

The barn is tucked away about 0.3 miles from the nearest road. It has a gas cooker, a wood burner, toilets and showers, but no electricity. BYO bedding, torch & candles. Pefect for groups of walkers, cyclists, runners and families wanting to explore the Dales.

    **GROUPS ONLY**

DETAILS
- **Open** - All year.
- **Beds** - 50
- **Price/night** - 36 people: £900 w/end. 50 people: £1,150 w/end. Enquire for prices for other party numbers.

CONTACT: Neil and Enid Caton,
Tel: 01729 822240
Hornby Laithe, Stainforth, Nr Settle,
North Yorkshire BD24 9PB

DETAILS
- **Open** - Spring, Summer & Autumn
- **Beds** - 16: 2x8 + camping
- **Price/night** - £10pp, £5pp for under 16s. Min stay 2 nights at £75pn.

CONTACT: Heather Hodgson
Tel: 01969 422145
raydalebarn@gmail.com
www.raydalebarn.co.uk
Busk Lane, Marsett Lane, Stalling Busk,
Leyburn, North Yorks DL8 3DH

INGLETON YHA
GRETA TOWER
167a

On the edge of the Yorkshire Dales, surrounded by magnificent countryside with caves, waterfalls and mountains, Ingleton is dominated by Ingleborough, the best known of Yorkshire's Three Peaks (this is a great base for The Challenge). Known for its walking routes and waterfall trail, the area has plenty for walkers, climbers, mountain bikers and cavers. Licensed and serving tasty meals there is also a self-catering kitchen. Perfect for families and school trips.

DETAILS
■ **Open** - All year. (Sole use only Nov-Feb). Reception open 8am-noon, 5-10pm
■ **Beds** - 64: 4x6, 7x4, 1x2, 2x5
■ **Price/night** - Beds from £18, rooms from £39. Sole use bookings welcome

CONTACT: Manager
Tel: 015242 41444
ingleton@yha.org.uk
www.ingletonhostel.co.uk
Greta Tower, Sammy Lane, Ingleton,
North Yorkshire, LA6 3EG

PUNCH BOWL
BUNKHOUSE & GLAMPING
167b

Nestling between the 3 National Parks of Forest of Bowland, Yorkshire Dales and the Lake District The Punch Bowl Hotel in Bentham provides B&B and camping.

Glamping tents and glamping pods will be also available early in 2020 and by the end of the year a new 20 bed bunkhouse will be open.

DETAILS
■ **Open** - All year
■ **Beds** - 66+ Bunkhouse 20: 2 rooms. B&B 6: 1x4 (family), 1x2 (dbl). Pods 10: 5x2. Tents 30: 5x6. Plus 15 pitches.
■ **Price/night** - All prices incl continental breakfast. Bunkhouse £25pp. Glamping Tents £25pp. Pods £35pp. B&B room £80 for 2 people plus £10pp in same room.

CONTACT:
Tel: 01524 298040
punchbowlhotel@yahoo.com
www.thepunchbowlbentham.co.uk
Punch Bowl Hotel, Eskew Lane, Low Bentham, North Yorkshire LA2 7DD

THE OLD SCHOOL
BUNKHOUSE
168

Situated near Ingleton in the Yorkshire Dales, on the Yorkshire Three Peaks route, The Old School Bunkhouse sleeps up to 28. It has a comfortable lounge, with TV, DVD & WiFi, a large kitchen diner, 4 bathrooms & a drying room with washing machine. Outside is parking for 12 cars and great views of Ingleborough and Whernside. The pub over the road is ideal for that celebratory drink.

       GROUPS ONLY

DETAILS

- **Open** - All year. 24 hours.
- **Beds** - 30: 4x6, 2x2 + 2 camp beds
- **Price/night** - Fri/Sat £400 per night (sole use) for up to 20 people + £18 per extra person. Min 2 nights at w/ends. Sun-Thurs £300 up to 20 + £15 per extra person. Max 30.

CONTACT: Debbie Bryant
Tel: 07909 223819
oldschoolbunkhouse@gmail.com
www.oldschoolbunkhouse.co.uk
Chapel-le-Dale, Ingleton, Carnforth, Lancs, LA6 3AR

BROADRAKE
BUNKBARN
169a

Broadrake Bunkbarn offers direct access to the Three Peaks Challenge Walk, The Pennine Journey & The Dales High Way.

This popular accommodation for 20 has an upstairs open-plan living space with excellent self-catering & communal facilities. Perfect for extended family reunions, cyclists, cavers and dark sky enthusiasts.
Indivudals, couples and small groups welcome mid-week.

DETAILS
- **Open** - All year. All day.
- **Beds** - 20: 1x8, 2x4, 2x twin.
- **Price/night** - Weekends: £900 for 2 nights sole use. Mid-week: £20pp or £360 a night sole use. £5pp bedding/towel hire.

CONTACT: Mike & Rachel Benson
Tel: 01524 241357
info@broadrake.co.uk
www.broadrake.co.uk
Broadrake, Chapel-le-Dale, Ingleton, LA6 3AX

GAUBER
BUNK BARN
169b

In the heart of Yorkshire's Three Peaks country right on the route between Pen-y-ghent & Whernside & close to the Dales Way, Dales High Way, Pennine Way & Pennine Bridleway. This warm comfortable bunk barn sleeps up to 13 in three bunk rooms. Living room with cosy wood burner, spacious well equipped kitchen & garden with stunning views. Group bookings only at w/ends. Book by the bed or room Sun-Thurs (not b/hols). Dogs & breakfast by arrangement. 4 bed annex also available.

DETAILS
- **Open** - All year. All day.
- **Beds** - 17: Bunkhouse: 13: 2x4, 1x5 (dbl+3) ensuite. The Den 4: 1x4.
- **Price/night** - £21 inc fitted sheet & pillow. Duvet & towel one off charge of £5.

CONTACT: Jon Radda & Katie Hawkins
Tel: 01524 241150
gauberbunkbarn@gmail.com
www.gauberbunkbarn.co.uk
Ribblehead, Ingleton, Carnforth, LA6 3JF

HOWGILLS
BARN

170

Howgills Barn offers a beautifully renovated self-catering barn in Sedbergh Yorkshire. Breathtaking views, plenty to see and do on the doorstep & set in a private location where the children can enjoy some freedom. A five minute walk into Sedbergh to nearby pubs, cafés and restaurants. Dogs welcome too. Hot tub available. Five stars on Trip Advisor from over 100 reviews gives a flavour of the quality of the accommodation.

DETAILS
- **Open** - All year. All day.
- **Beds** - 35: 6x4 1x5 1x6 (all en suite) plus camping
- **Price/night** - Prices start (midweek) from £30 per person.

CONTACT: Dawn or Amy
Tel: 08008 321632
info@howgillsaccommodation.co.uk
www.howgillsaccommodation.co.uk
Castlehaw Farm, Castlehaw Lane,
Sedbergh, Cumbria LA10 5BA

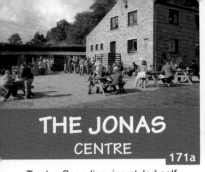

THE JONAS
CENTRE

171a

DALES
BIKE CENTRE

171b

Twelve Scandinavian styled self-catering log cabins located at the heart of Wensleydale in the tranquil beauty of the Yorkshire Dales,. Nine lodges are located in Elm Wood away from the main complex & the other three are located near to Granary Barn, which has a shop, two lounges a meeting room and a kitchen for group use. The varied use of the centre means that facilities are comfortable rather than luxurious.

Dales Bike Centre, Swaledale, is the centre of cycling in Yorkshire! Home of the Ard Rock Enduro, en-route of the 2014 Tour de France Grand Depart, the 2019 World Road Race Championship's route, the Yorkshire Dales Cycle Way and loads of great cycling & mountain biking. On-site café, bike shop, MTB, road & e-bike hire, bike wash, workshop, drying room & lots of friendly advice.
Close to 4 pubs & Reeth village.

DETAILS

- **Open** - All year. Office open from 9am - 5pm Monday to Saturday.
- **Beds** - 60: 12 lodges each sleeping between 5 and 7 people.
- **Price/night** - See website for special offers. Discounts for full site use.

DETAILS

- **Open** - All year. All day.
- **Beds** - 14: Old Barn 1x4, 1x2. New Barn 1x4, 2x2,
- **Price/night** - Single room £39, 2 bed bunkroom £58, 4 bed bunkroom £116, 3 people in 4 bed bunkroom £97. Inc b/fast.

CONTACT: Simon Eastwood
Tel: 01969 624900
stay@jonascentre.org
www.jonascentre.org
Redmire, Leyburn. North Yorkshire,
DL8 4EW

CONTACT: Stu Price
Tel: 01748 884908
enquiries@dalesbikecentre.co.uk
www.dalesbikecentre.co.uk
Parks Barn, Fremington, Richmond,
Yorkshire Dales DL11 6AW

KIRKBY STEPHEN
HOSTEL
172a

NEW ING
LODGE
172b

Former Methodist Church with a range of accommodation for individuals, families and groups amongst beautiful authentic features; stained glass, arches and panels. There's a large dining room & kitchen and a quiet lounge in the gallery. Kirkby Stephen is a market town in the upper Eden Valley. On Wainwright's Coast to Coast path with easy access to the Pennine Journey, the W2W cycle route, the Howgill Hills, the Yorkshire Dales and the Lake District.

This 10-bedroom, 10-bathroom B&B & hostel offers comfortable, friendly, accommodation with delicious food. Shap is in the Eden Valley, just off the M6, on the edge of the Lake District National Park. The Howgills & the Pennine Fells are close by. On Wainwright's Coast to Coast, the Westmorland Way & the Miller's Way it's perfect for large groups or individuals.

DETAILS

DETAILS

- **Open** - All year. Please arrive after 5pm (or ring to arrange arrival).
- **Beds** - 38: 1x8, 3x6, 2x4, 1x2, 1x2 en suite.
- **Price/night** - £24.50pp

- **Open** - All year.
- **Beds** - 30: 4xdbl, 2xfamily (dbl + 2 singles), 2xtriple, 2x4-bedded dormitory
- **Price/night** - £20pp dorm. B&B (private rooms) from £55pp. Discounts for larger groups/longer stays. Sole use from only £600.

CONTACT: Denise
Tel: 07812 558525
kirkbystephenhostel@btconnect.com
www.kirkbystephenhostel.co.uk
Market Street, Kirkby Stephen, Cumbria,
CA17 4QQ

CONTACT: Scott
Tel: 01931 716719
info@newinglodge.co.uk
www.newinglodge.co.uk
New Ing Lodge, Main Street, Shap,
Penrith, Cumbria, CA10 3LX

GREENGILL
BARN
173

A converted traditional barn on the edge of Morland in Cumbria's rolling Eden Valley. Close to the Lake District and handy for the M6. Great for gatherings of family or friends wanting to visit the Lake District, the Pennines, the Yorkshire Dales and the Borders. There is a large, fully equipped kitchen/dining room and a large, two-storey games room. On NCR 71 and Wiggo's Loop on C2C. Good local walking and easy access to lakes & fells. Local café and pub for meals & ale.

DETAILS

- **Open** - All year.
- **Beds** - 16: 2x8
- **Price/night** - Min 2 nights: £640 then £160 per night. Own sleeping bags free, or duvet, pillow, towel £10. Dogs £20.

CONTACT: Freddy Markham
Tel: 01931 714244 or 07831 428541
freddy@greengillholidays.co.uk
www.greengillholidays.co.uk
Greengill Barn, Strickland Road,
Morland, Penrith, Cumbria CA10 3AX

HUMPHREY HEAD
GROUP HOSTEL
174

Perched on an outcrop overlooking Morecambe Bay on the edge of The Lake District, Humphrey Head Group Hostel & Outdoor Centre is perfect for family celebrations, reunions, stag/hen parties, schools, clubs & groups.

Remote & private, surrounded by stunning scenery & nature, with outdoor activities on site there is something for everyone. Catering & camping available.

       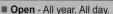 **GROUPS ONLY**

DETAILS
- **Open** - All year. All day.
- **Beds** - 66: 3x8,3x6,5x4,1x2,1x2 sgles
- **Price/night** - Sole use: Groups up to 20: Mon-Fri £1860, Fri-Sat £1260. 1 night £900. Please enquire for larger groups.

CONTACT: Becky or Susie
Tel: 015395 35030
info@meremountains.co.uk
humphreyhead.education
Humphrey Head O.C, Holy Well Lane,
Flookburgh, Cumbria LA11 7LY

YEALAND
OLD SCHOOL
175a

175b
HIGH WALLABARROW
CAMPING BARN

Yeland Old School provides newly refurbished, self-catering accommodation with en suite bedrooms and group dorms. Relax in the grounds of the Quaker Meeting House. A short stroll from Summerhouse Hill and Warton Crag amidst spectacular limestone scenery and nature reserves. LEJOG passes the front door on Route 6. Quiet village location with pub serving food.

High Wallabarrow is a traditional hill farm in the Duddon Valley, the Lake District's quiet corner. The well equipped camping barn, an old farmhouse, sleeps 10 upstairs. Downstairs there's a large living area with woodburning stove and fully equipped kitchen. Mattresses provided BYO sleeping bags/pillows. Toilet just outside and shower nearby. 15 mins' walk to pub, 10 mins to climbing crag. Not suitable for rowdy groups.

DETAILS
- **Open** - All year. Check in between 5-8pm (or by arrangement) Depart by 11am.
- **Beds** - 25: 1x2, 2x4, 10x stacking beds, 5 x mats
- **Price/night** - From £20pp, £10 children 5+. Sole use from £150.

CONTACT: Alison Smedley
Tel: 0333 0065295
yealandoldschool@gmail.com
www.yealandoldschool.co.uk
18 Yealand Rd, Yealand Conyers, Carnforth, Lancashire LA5 9SH

DETAILS
- **Open** - All year. Arrive after 4pm, (earlier by arrangement) vacate by 11am.
- **Beds** - 10: 1x10 with extra possible.
- **Price/night** - £12.50pp weeknights in school term. Two-night weekends sole-use £125/night. £1.50 per dog per night..

CONTACT: Chris Chinn (9am to 9pm)
Tel: 01229 715011
camden.chinn@gmail.com
www.wallabarrow.co.uk
High Wallabarrow, Ulpha, Broughton-in-Furness, Cumbria, LA20 6EA

WITHERSLACK
CYCLE BARN

176

Located between Grange Over Sands and Kendal on the northern shore of Morecambe Bay. The bunkhouse is within the beautiful Whitbarrow Nature Reserve in the southern Lake District. Built for cyclists and walkers with drying room, laundry, communal kitchen, diner, lounges, secure cycle storage, workshop and bike wash. Perfect for groups, families and individuals. Just 500m from the Morecambe 'Bay Cycle Way', the Lakes & Dales Loop and NCN 700 & 70 E-bike hire is available on site.

DETAILS

- **Open** - All year. All day
- **Beds** - 14: 2x2(twin) 1x4(family), 1x6.
- **Price/night** - From £20. £2 towel hire Food on request.

CONTACT: Steph Fry
Tel: 01539 552223
info@beckhead.co.uk
www.witherslackcyclebarn.co.uk
Beck Head Farm, Witherslack, Grange
Over Sands. Cumbria, LA11 6SH

ROOKHOW
BUNKBARN
177

Set in 12 acres of its own ancient woodland, Rookhow provides a simple and comfortable retreat for families, friends and groups. A small, cosy hostel converted from stables of the nearby Quaker Meeting House (available as an extra space for group activities). Near Coniston, Windermere & Grizedale Forest. Rookhow is the perfect base for walking, mountain biking or for workshops or training events.

     GROUPS ONLY

DETAILS
- **Open** - All year. All day.
- **Beds** - 16: in 3 rooms + camping.
- **Price/night** - £250 (min 2nights). Plus £50 per night for Quaker Meeting House. Camping extra: £10 adult, £5 child.

CONTACT: Sue Nicholls
Tel: 07557 919879
rookhow.org.uk
www.rookhowcentre.co.uk
Rookhow, Rusland, nr Grizedale, Ulverston, South Lakeland, Cumbria
LA12 8LA

LOWICK SCHOOL
BUNKHOUSE
178

Within the old primary school at Lowick Green, nestled between Coniston water(4 miles) and Ulverston, the bunkhouse has a lounge with wood-burning stove, large kitchen/dining room, great views of the mountains and an outdoor area with campfire. River Deep Mountain High Activity Centre provides a wide variety of outdoor activities. Group and family packages include activities in the price.

        GROUPS ONLY

DETAILS

- **Open** - All year.
- **Beds** - 20: 2x8, 1x4 (one 8 bed can be expanded to 10)
- **Price/night** - Sole use from £600 at weekends (Club scheme), from £220 per night Mon-Thurs. £250 damage deposit. Family holiday packages.

CONTACT: Emma Hoving
Tel: 01539 528666
info@riverdeepmountainhigh.co.uk
riverdeepmountainhigh.co.uk
Lowick Green, Ulverston, LA12 8EB

HIGH WRAY
BASECAMP

Situated in the heart of South Lakeland, in secluded woodland, just 4 miles from the popular tourist village of Ambleside, High Wray Basecamp provides an ideal base for groups wishing to explore the Lake District. Perfect for rambling, fell walking, climbing and water sports. The Basecamp ranger will happily advise on local walks and activities. The Longland block has 2 dorms each sleeping 8, while the Acland block has 2 dorms each sleeping 10 and a leaders' room.

        GROUPS ONLY

DETAILS

■ **Open** - All year. All day.
■ **Beds** - 38: Longland 16: 2x8. Acland 22: 2x10, 1x2
■ **Price/night** - Prices from £11 per person per night (min 8 persons).

CONTACT: Philippa Barber
Tel: 01539 434633
Philippa.barber@nationaltrust.org.uk
www.nationaltrust.org.uk/holidays
High Wray, Ambleside, Cumbria, Lake
District. LA22 0JE

LAKE DISTRICT
BACKPACKERS
180a

KENDAL
HOSTEL
180b

In the heart of Windermere, close to shops, cafés and pubs, 2 minutes from the train & bus station and opposite the TIC and tour offices. Easy access to the National Park by the 555 bus, 25 minute walk to the lake with steamer trips and boat hire and access to the fells from the door. Maps and guides available in this friendly, cosy hostel.

Kendal Hostel, a Georgian townhouse in the historic market town of Kendal, is next to the well known Brewery Arts Centre and only a stone's throw from the town centre. Facilities include 13 bedrooms for up to 65 guests, kitchen, lounge, dining room, bike shed and free WiFi. Single/double/family/group rooms plus mixed & single sex dorms.

DETAILS

- **Open** - All year. 24 hours with key code for front door.
- **Beds** - 20:- 1x6, 2x4, 2 x double with single above.
- **Price/night** - From £16.95pp dorms, £19.95pp private rooms. £2pn discount for stays of 3+ nights (Nov-Mar) inc self serve continental b-fast & free tea/coffee.

DETAILS

- **Open** - All year. 8-11.30am, 4-8.30pm and by arrangement.
- **Beds** - 65: 1x12, 1x8, 2x7(fam), 2x6, 1x5(fam), 1x4, 1x3, 3x2, 1xdbl. Family rooms have a private shower room & double bed. Single rooms available also.
- **Price/night** - £20 Sun -Thurs, £22 Fri & Sat. Sole use from £700 per night.

CONTACT: Paul
Tel: 01539 446374
info@lakedistrictbackpackers.co.uk
www.lakedistrictbackpackers.co.uk
High Street, Windermere, Cumbria,
LA23 1AF

CONTACT: Jan or Kristina
Tel: 01539 724066
kristina@kendalhostel.co.uk
www.kendalhostel.com
118-120 Highgate, Kendal, Cumbria,
LA9 4HE

DACRES STABLE
CAMPING BARN
181a

A short drive from Kendal, Dacres Stable Camping Barn is on the eastern edge of the Lake District National Park. On a gated road away from the main A6 it is a perfect base for exploring the Yorkshire Dales, the Lake District and the Eden Valley. Great too for mountain biking, walking, & cycling on quiet tracks and lanes. The camping barn comfortably sleeps 8 on a sole use, self-catering basis.

DETAILS
- **Open** - Easter to November inclusive
- **Beds** - 8: 1x2 1x6.
- **Price/night** - Sole use of the building. Ground floor only (sleeps 2 + 1) £55. Ground floor plus upper bunk room £80. Minimum 2 nights stay. Reductions for longer stays.

CONTACT: Hilary Fell
Tel: 01539 823208 or 07788 633936
dacresstablecampingbarn.blogspot.com
Grisedale Farm, Whinfell, Kendal, Cumbria, LA8 9EN

THORNEY HOW
181b

Thorney How offers clean, comfortable accommodation in Grasmere. Family-run and welcoming it provides en suite, simple B&B and self-catering. Close to the Coast to Coast path, local village and lake. Your perfect Lake District base. A bar, restaurant and spacious grounds complete the experience.

DETAILS
- **Open** - All year. Closed 10.30am to 3.30pm. Check in 3.30-10.30pm.
- **Beds** - 42: Main House 26, 2xdbl, 1xtwin, 2x4, 2x6. Bunkhouse 16
- **Price/night** - Dble en suite B&B from £82. Family en-suite B&B from £100. 4 person budget rooms from £80. Larger catered groups please enquire.

CONTACT: Taylor Nuttall
Tel: 01539 435597
enquiries@thorneyhow.co.uk
www.thorneyhow.co.uk
Thorney How, Off Helm Close & Easedale Rd, Grasmere, Cumbria, LA22 9QW

RYDAL HALL
BUNKHOUSE

Situated next to Rydal Beck in the heart of the Lake District, Rydal Hall Bunkhouse provides accommodation for groups of up to 29 in four dormitories plus a large common room, drying room & a fully equipped stainless steel kitchen.

There is also a quiet campsite for individuals and families, eco-pods in the grounds and en suite accommodation for up to 50 in the main hall and a tea shop.

GROUPS ONLY

DETAILS

■ **Open** - All year. All day.

■ **Beds** - Bunkhouse 29: 1x10, 1x9, 1x6, 1x4. Plus campsite, eco-pods, accommodation for 50 in the main hall.

■ **Price/night** - Youth Centre £315. Discounts & late deals possible. Pods £47.50, £42pn 2+ nights, £37pn 4+ nights.

CONTACT: Bookings Office
Tel: 01539 432050
mail@rydalhall.org
www.rydalhall.org
Rydal Hall, Ambleside, Cumbria,
LA22 9LX

ELTERWATER
HOSTEL
183

Located in the peaceful village of Elterwater, in the Langdale valley, 15 mins' drive from Ambleside. The area has many walks for people of all abilities, from gentle riverside meanders to the challenge presented by the Langdale Pikes, Bowfell and Scafell. Pubs, shops and other amenities are nearby. The area is popular for both on and off-road cycling, rock climbing and other outdoor activities. An ideal overnight stop on the Cumbria Way.

DETAILS
- **Open** - All year (Nov-Feb groups only). Access 7.30am-11.30pm. Reception open 7.30-10am and 5-10.30pm.
- **Beds** - 38 : 6x2, 1x4, 1x4 ensuite, 3x6
- **Price/night** - £20-£29 pp, check website for special offers.Call for sole use.

CONTACT: Nick Owen
Tel: 01539 437245
bookings@elterwaterhostel.co.uk
www.elterwaterhostel.co.uk
Elterwater, Ambleside LA22 9HX

GREAT LANGDALE
BUNKHOUSE

Great Langdale Bunkhouse is situated amidst some of the finest mountain scenery in England with access to mountain biking, cycling, walking, fell running and climbing.

The bunkhouse has 18 single beds divided into 3 twin rooms and 2 rooms of six (all bunk beds). The rooms are simple but comfortable and each room has a double plug socket. The bunkhouse has biomass central heating throughout so its toasty warm with an endless supply of hot water and powerful showers.

DETAILS

- **Open** - All year. All day.
- **Beds** - 18: 2x6, 3x2
- **Price/night** - From £15 per person.

CONTACT: Ben or Sabrina
langdale.bunkhouse@gmail.com
www.greatlangdalebunkhouse.co.uk
Great Langdale, Ambleside,
Cumbria, LA22 9JU

SHEPHERDS
CROOK

Noran Bank Farm is near Ullswater just through Patterdale in Cumbria, just 5 minutes' walk away from the Coast to Coast route and The Westmorland Way. Shepherd's Crook Bunkhouse is a barn converted to a very high standard and sleeps 8. Duvets, linen and towels are provided. DIY breakfast and packed lunches can be pre-booked. It is very popular with Coast to Coasters, walkers, cyclists and for family/friends get-togethers.

DETAILS

- **Open** - All year.
- **Beds** - 8: 1x6, 1x2 + B&B.
- **Price/night** - £18pp (6 bed room), £22pp (double room). Sole use £140. Farmhouse B&B £32.50pp.

CONTACT: Mrs Heather Jackson
Tel: 01768 482327 or 07833 981504
heathernoranbank@gmail.com
www.noranbankfarm.co.uk
Noran Bank Farm, Patterdale, Penrith, Cumbria, CA11 0NR

FISHER GILL
CAMPING BARN
186

Situated in Thirlmere at the foot of the Helvellyn mountains, close to Sticks Pass & the spectacular Fisher-Gill waterfall, the barn has direct access to numerous walks, hill & rock climbing. It is just off the A591 with local & national bus stops at the end of the lane. Accommodation consists of two rooms; a kitchen/diner with all the basic equipment & a 10 bed bunkroom (BYO sleeping bag). A pub serving meals is a short walk away. Perfect for quiet country retreats, but not suitable for noisy groups. No mobile phone signal or WiFi.

DETAILS
- **Open** - All year. Check in by 9pm.
- **Beds** - 10
- **Price/night** - £16pp. Sole use £160.

CONTACT: Louise Hodgson
Tel: 017687 74391 or 017687 73232
stybeckfarm@btconnect.com
www.stybeckfarm.co.uk
Stybeck Farm, Thirlmere, Keswick,
Cumbria CA12 4TN

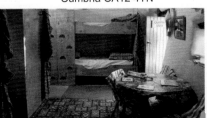

ST JOHNS IN THE VALE
CAMPING BARN

St John's-in-the-Vale Camping Barn is an 18th century stable on a peaceful hill farm, with stunning views to Blencathra, Helvellyn and Castle Rock.

The Barn has a sleeping area upstairs (mattresses provided) and a sitting/dining area below. A separate toilet, shower and cooking area (BYO equipment) are within the building. A wood-burning stove makes it nice and cosy. Outside there is a BBQ area. As there is no light pollution, the star-filled night skies are magical.

DETAILS

- **Open** - All year. All day.
- **Beds** - 8 : 1x8 + camping
- **Price/night** - Barn £11pp. Camping £5.50pp

CONTACT: Sarah
Tel: 017687 79242 (Book 017687 74301)
info@campingbarn.com
www.campingbarn.com
Low Bridge End Farm, St John's-in-the-Vale, Keswick, CA12 4TS

THE WHITE HORSE
INN BUNKHOUSE
188

The White Horse Inn has 2 bunkhouses in the converted stables of this traditional Lake District inn at the foot of Blencathra. Guests are welcome in the Inn which has great pub food, open fires, local ales and is open from 11am to 11pm. Each bunkhouse has a basic kitchen, dining area and bunkrooms sleeping between 4 and 6. Paths to the mountains from the garden & the C2C route passes the door.

DETAILS

- **Open** - All year. All day access.
- **Beds** - 50:1x8,3x6,6x4 (2 bunkhouses)
- **Price/night** - £12pp. Private rooms: 4 bed £48, 6 bed £72, 8 bed £96. Sole use of 24 bed bunkhouse £260. Sole use of 26 bed bunkhouse £280. Bedding £5/stay. Enquire for Xmas/New Year.

CONTACT: Phil or Cozmin
Tel: 017687 79883
info@thewhitehorse-blencathra.co.uk
www.thewhitehorse-blencathra.co.uk
The White Horse Inn, Scales, Nr
Threlkeld, Keswick, CA12 4SY

LOWSIDE FARM
CAMPING BARN & PODS
189

Nestling at the foot of Blencathra, with paths to the mountains from the doorstep Lowside Farm Camping Barn & Pods are your perfect Lake District base.

Sleeping groups of up to 14, the newly converted camping barn is modern & comfortable, The six, 4 berth luxury camping pods, provide extra accommodation for larger groups, older family members and those with small chilldren. All bedding is provided.

DETAILS

- **Open** - All year
- **Beds** - 38: Bunkhouse 14: 1x12,1x2. Pods 24: 6x4
- **Price/night** - £25pp. Min 8 people. Min 2 nights.

CONTACT:
Tel: 7887645229
microlodges@btinternet.com
lowsidefarm.co.uk
Lowside Farm, Troutbeck, Penrith,
Cumbria CA11 0SX

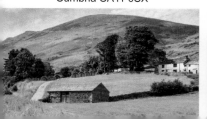

BLAKEBECK FARM
CAMPING BARN
190a

190b
BASSENTHWAITE
PARISH ROOM

At the foot of Souther Fell, within easy reach of Blencathra, Blakebeck Farm is set amidst the wildflower meadows of Mungrisdale. On the C2C cycle route & the Cumbrian Way. Perfect as a weekend break for walkers. The large upstairs room has bunk beds for 10 people (BYO sleeping bags) & a large farmhouse table. The kitchen has all you need to cook a simple meal, electric hob, microwave, toaster, fridge & kettle. One dog with sole use only by prior arrangement. Not suitable for parties.

Refurbished to a very high standard, the Parish Room is a great base for outdoors enthusiasts to explore Skiddaw the Northern Lakes, Keswick and the Cumbrian coast.

There is a modern well-equipped kitchen large hall, meeting room with sofa and large TV. There is also disabled access throughout. Separate male/female toilets and two shower rooms. Bring your own beds, bedding and towels. Free WiFi. Sorry no stag/hen parties.

DETAILS

- **Open** - All year. All day
- **Beds** - 10: 1x10 + holiday cottages
- **Price/night** - £12 pp. Sole use £120

CONTACT: Judith
Tel: Booking Office 017687 74301 Farm
017687 79957 Mob 07789 287121
j.egan001@btinternet.com
blakebeckfarm.co.uk
Blakebeck, Mungrisdale, Penrith,
CA11 0SZ

DETAILS

- **Open** - All year
- **Beds** - 18 (BYO beds/bedding/towels)
- **Price/night** - £180 for 18 people (larger and smaller groups please get in touch for price). Two night minimum stay.

CONTACT: Louise
bookbassenthwaiteparishroom@gmail.com
www.bassenthwaite.org.uk
School Road, Bassenthwaite, Keswick,
CA12 4QJ

LONSCALE HOSTEL
FSC BLENCATHRA
191

Beautifully situated on the south facing slopes of Blencathra just 1 mile out of the Lakeland village of Threlkeld, Lonscale is a new hostel offering group accommodation at the FSC Blencathra Centre.

Groups of 14-26 can have sole use of this award winning eco-friendly accommodation. There are also 4 self catering cottages and a 110 bed educational centre on this site.

 GROUPS ONLY

DETAILS

■ **Open** - All year
■ **Beds** - 26: 1x6, 1x4, 3x3, 2x2, 1xdbl, 1x1 (all en suite)
■ **Price/night** - From £19 pp. Min group size 14

CONTACT: FSC Blencathra
Tel: 017687 79601
enquiries.bl@field-studies-council.org
www.field-studies-council.org
FSC Blencathra, Blease Road, Threlkeld, Keswick, Cumbria. CA12 4SG

SKIDDAW HOUSE
HOSTEL
192a

DENTON
HOUSE
192b

The highest hostel in Britain! Escape the crowds at this remote mountain hostel.

No roads, no other buildings, no phone signal, just uninterrupted beautiful mountain views. But there's no need to compromise on comfort, with wood burning stoves, hot showers, a well-stocked bar and full bedding provided. An easy walk or mountain bike ride from Keswick or Threlkeld.

Denton House is a purpose built hostel and outdoor centre in the Lake District offering bunkhouse accommodation. Warm and well equipped for self-catering, the centre was designed for groups with parking for 40 cars. A variety of outdoor activities can be arranged on site. There is equipment storage and access to the River Greta across the road.

DETAILS

■ **Open** - March-Nov. Groups only between Nov-March. Check in from 5pm.
■ **Beds** - 22 : 1 x 8, 2 x 5, 1 x 4
■ **Price/night** - Dorm bed from £20. Private rooms from £50. Camping from £10. Hire the whole hostel from £300.

DETAILS

■ **Open** - All year (including Christmas). Office hours 9am - 8pm.
■ **Beds** - 56: 1x4, 2x6, 1x8, 2x10, 1x12.
■ **Price/night** - £19 midweek, £22 weekend. Sole use £900 (midweek). Breakfast £6. Pack lunch £6. Dinner £10. Activities £30/half day.

CONTACT: Martin or Suzy
Tel: 07747 174293
info@skiddawhouse.co.uk
www.skiddawhouse.co.uk
Bassenthwaite, Keswick, Cumbria,
CA12 4QX

CONTACT: Libby Scott
Tel: 01768 775351
keswickhostel@hotmail.co.uk
www.dentonhouse-keswick.co.uk
Penrith Road, Keswick, Cumbria,
CA12 4JW

DERWENTWATER
INDEPENDENT HOSTEL
193

Family run and friendly, Derwentwater Independent Hostel is a Georgian mansion in 17 acres of grounds with stunning mountain views. Just 2 miles from Keswick, close to the Coast to Coast route and the delights of Borrowdale, it makes a great base for individuals, families, groups and conferences. The hostel has plenty of space in & out for you to use and relax in. Home-made food is available.

DETAILS

- **Open** - All year. 7am - 11pm.
- **Beds** - 88: 1x4, 2x5, 3x6, 3x8, 1x10, 1x22
- **Price/night** - From £22.00 (adult), £17.00 (child). Family rooms from £76 (for 4). Ask if you want a room for 2 or 3.

CONTACT:
Tel: 01768 777246
reception@derwentwater.org
www.derwentwater.org
Barrow House, Borrowdale, Keswick, Cumbria, CA12 5UR

HAWSE END
CENTRE
194

Hawse End Centre sits at the head of the magnificent Borrowdale Valley on the shores of Derwentwater with easy access to Keswick via launch or lakeside walk. The house is a large, comfortable, country mansion, ideal for large groups, while the Cottage is more suited to smaller group, families and individuals. For the more adventurous there are two yurts with stunning views and transparent domes for star gazing.

Catering & outdoor activities with instruction can be booked in advance.

DETAILS
- **Open** - All year.
- **Beds** - House 49: (9 rooms). Cottage 24: (6 rooms). Yurts: 24 (2x12)
- **Price/night** - Enquire for prices.

CONTACT:
Tel: 01768 812280
cumbriaoutdoors.enquiries@cumbria.gov.uk
www.cumbria.gov.uk/cumbriaoutdoors
Portinscale, Keswick, Cumbria,
CA12 5UE

WATENDLATH
BOTHY
195

Watendlath Bothy sits next to the tarn in the quiet, picturesque hamlet that shares its name. High in a beautiful valley, it offers superb access to the surrounding fells. Visitors should treat the Bothy as a stone tent, BYO equipment as for camping, such as cutlery, plates, sleeping bags & mats, matches.

The perfect choice for people looking to escape to one of the most remote-feeling places in the Lake District.

DETAILS
- **Open** - Mid March- Mid October
- **Beds** - 6: BYO mats and sleeping bags
- **Price/night** - Low season: £60/night High season: £70/night. Minimum 3 nights.

CONTACT: National Trust Holidays
Tel: 0344 335 1296
bunkhouses@nationaltrust.org.uk
www.nationaltrust.org.uk/holidays
Watendlath, Borrowdale, Cumbria,
CA12 5UW

BOWDERSTONE
BUNKHOUSE
196a

HIGH HOUSE
196b

Bowderstone Bunkhouse is situated along the Borrowdale Valley by the famous Bowderstone – a massive boulder that has lain precariously on one side for the last 10,000 years! It has a kitchen, accessible shower room and communal area, plus running water, electricity and drainage, but linen and mattresses not provided. Please note, Bowderstone Bunkhouse is only for use by clubs, educational groups or other organisations such as the Scouts, as it is on National Trust land and has certain restrictions to its use.

High House in Seathwaite, at the head of the beautiful valley of Borrowdale, offers comfortable bunkhouse/hostel accommodation. Popular with walking and climbing clubs and educational groups, early booking is advised. Two dorms are available each with toilet, washbasin and shower. There is a third dorm reserved for K Fellfarers members and club members may use this room during your stay. If you wish to have exclusive use, including this Members Room, there's a £25 supplement per night.

        GROUPS ONLY

       GROUPS ONLY

DETAILS

- **Open** - All year.
- **Beds** - 12
- **Price/night** - £100 per night

DETAILS

- **Open** - All year. All day.
- **Beds** - 26: 1x18, 1x8
- **Price/night** - £166, or £191 if exclusive occupancy required (weekdays only).

CONTACT: Reception at the Lake District Calvert Trust
Tel: 017687 72255
enquiries@calvertlakes.org.uk
www.calvertlakes.org.uk
Grange, Keswick, CA12 5XA

CONTACT: Hugh Taylor
Tel: 01524 762067
jhugh.taylor@btinternet.com
highhouseborrowdale.co.uk
Seathwaite, Borrowdale, Keswick.

CRAGG
CAMPING BARN

Cragg Camping Barn, with stunning views of the Buttermere Fells, is a great base for all outdoor enthusiasts with great walking, climbing and mountain biking close by. Sleeps 8 with a kitchen and seating area, hot shower on a meter and toilet/ washbasin with hot and cold water. BYO sleeping bag and stove/ eating utensils if you wish to self-cater. Under-5's and dogs welcome (sole occupancy only). Cragg House Farm also has a holiday cottage sleeping two.

DETAILS

- **Open** - All year. Arrival from 4pm, late arrivals by arrangement.
- **Beds** - 8: 1 x 8
- **Price/night** - £12 per person.

CONTACT: John and Vicki Temple
Tel: Camping Barn 01768 774301 Farm and Cottage 01768 770204
info@lakelandcampingbarns.co.uk
www.buttermerecottage.co.uk
Cragg House Farm, Buttermere, Cockermouth, Cumbria, CA13 9XA

LOW GILLERTHWAITE
FIELD CENTRE
198a

THE WILD WOOL
BARN
198b

In the Ennerdale Valley, one of the most beautiful, least spoilt and quietest in the Lake District, Low GIllerthwaite Field Centre sits at the foot of Pillar and Red Pike. Well equipped for groups it is the perfect base for fell walking, rock climbing, bird & wildlife watching, mountain biking, orienteering & canoeing. The centre generates its own hydro-electricity. Vehicle access is by forest track and a BT payphone is on site as most mobiles do not work here.

Nestled in the peace of the Ennerdale Valley, overlooking Ennerdale Water, The Wild Wool Barn provides luxury bunkhouse accommodation for 6 (plus 6 camping). Traditional wood-burning stove, electric heating, cooker and shower marry tradition with luxury. With no mobile signal or WiFi The Wild Wool Barn is a true chance to get away and explore the rarely visited Western Lakes.

DETAILS

■ **Open** - All year (except Christmas and Boxing Day). 24 hours.
■ **Beds** - 40: 2x4, 1x8, 1x10, 1x14.
■ **Price/night** - From £11.50 per person (children and students), £15.50 (adults), camping is £5 per person.

CONTACT: Ellen or Walter
Tel: 01946 861229
Warden@lgfc.org.uk
www.lgfc.org.uk
Ennerdale, Cleator, CA23 3AX

DETAILS

■ **Open** - All year.
■ **Beds** - 6: 1x6 + 6 camping
■ **Price/night** - High season (for 6) from 1 night £130 to 7 nights £525. Exclusive use including 6 camping: from 1 night £182 to 7 nights £889. Bank hols min 3 nights. Low season (Nov-March) 1-3 people £60 per night, Camping £10pp.

CONTACT: Susan Denham-Smith
Tel: 01946 861270
susan@wildwoolworkshop.co.uk
www.wildwoolbarn.co.uk
Routen Farm Cot, Ennerdale, CA23 3AU

HOLME WOOD
BOTHY

Holme Wood Bothy offers basic accommodation in a spectacular secluded location, right on the shore of Loweswater. This stone tent provides a roof, kitchen and sleeping platform. Visitors must bring all camping equipment including plates, matches, sleeping mats & bags, food & water.

If you are looking for a remote and basic getaway with easy access to the lake, this bothy is your perfect choice. Great for canoeing on Loweswater.

DETAILS

- **Open** - All year. All day.
- **Beds** - 6- BYO mats and sleeping bag.
- **Price/night** - Low season: £60/night High season: £70/night

CONTACT: National Trust Holidays
Tel: 0344 335 1296
bunkhouses@nationaltrust.org.uk
www.nationaltrust.org.uk
Watergate Farm, Loweswater,
Cockermouth, Cumbria, CA13 0RU

CALDBECK
GLAMPING BARNS
200a

HILLSIDE FARM
BUNKBARN
200b

Opening Summer 2020, Caldbeck Glamping accommodation is in the centre of Caldbeck Village close to Wainwright's Northern Fells. Opposite The Odd Fellows pub and close to the village store and craft centre.
The self contained barns and cottage sleep 8, 4, 4, and 2 and there is also space for 2 tents. Caldbeck is a 25 minute drive from M6 motorway and right on The Cumbria Way walk and The Reivers Cycle route.

A Georgian farmstead, still a working farm, right on Hadrian's Wall National Trail and Cycleway near the Solway Coast AONB. Stunning views over the Solway Firth marshes towards Scotland. Bunkbarn or B&B rooms available. The bunkbarn, in a converted stable block, has cooking facilities & hot showers. Towels and sleeping bags can be hired. The bunk barn is heated with a bio mass boiler. Breakfast or bacon sandwiches available with notice. Walking, cycling and family groups are most welcome.

DETAILS
- **Open** - Opening Summer 2020
- **Beds** - 18: 8:1x8, 4:1x4, 4:1x4, 2:1xdbl
- **Price/night** - High Pike £204, Carrock Fell £104, The Cottage £110, The Bothy £60.

DETAILS
- **Open** - All year. 10am to 9pm.
- **Beds** - 12
- **Price/night** - £13pp inc shower. £4 full english, £2.50 hot sandwiches.

CONTACT: John Nicoll
Tel: 07410 694305
info@caldbeckglamping.co.uk
caldbeckglamping.co.uk
Caldbeck, Lake District, Cumbria,
CA7 8DZ

CONTACT: Mrs Sandra Rudd
Tel: 01228 576398
ruddshillside1@btinternet.com
www.hadrianswalkbnb.co.uk
Hillside Farm, Boustead Hill, Burgh-by-Sands, Carlisle, Cumbria, CA5 6AA

WAYFARERS
INDEPENDENT HOSTEL
201a

CARLISLE
CITY HOSTEL
201b

Close to Penrith town centre and perfect for the C2C cycle route.

Excellent value accommodation to those visiting Penrith, the Eden Valley and the North Lake District National Park. Bike cleaning and maintenance facilities and bike hire on site. Full kitchen and dining facilities, en suite rooms with made up beds, lockers, bedside lights. Individuals, small parties and groups welcome.

Carlisle's only independent hostel. Located on picturesque Abbey Street, the building is an old Georgian terrace accommodating up to 20 guests. There is a communal kitchen, lounge with TV, DVDs & book swap and a dining room. Free tea, coffee and WiFi . Prices include a basic breakfast. A great place from which to explore Carlisle, the Tuille House Museum, the Eden Valley, Hadrian's Wall and more. The staff look forward to welcoming you as their guest to the hostel & the city.

DETAILS
- **Open** - Feb-Dec. Reception open 8-11am, 4-9pm.
- **Beds** - 18: 2x2 (twin), 1x6, 2x4.
- **Price/night** - From £23pp (dorm room bed). Sole use from £370pn. Family room: Sun-Thurs from £60. B/fast: £5.Towel: £1.

CONTACT: Zahava and Ben
Tel: 01768 866011
guests@wayfarershostel.com
www.wayfarershostel.com
19 Brunswick Square, Penrith, Cumbria, CA11 7LR

DETAILS
- **Open** - All year. Check in between 3pm- 8pm ONLY. (Sunday 4pm-8pm).
- **Beds** - 20 : 2x6, 2x4.
- **Price/night** - £18 to £26 pp. Groups of over 8 by pre-arrangement only.

CONTACT: Jonathan Quinlan
Tel: 07914 720821
info@carlislecityhostel.com
www.carlislecityhostel.com
36 Abbey Street, Carlisle, CA3 8TX

HAGGS BANK

BUNKHOUSE & CAMPING

In the stunning North Pennines AONB, England's last wilderness, perfect for lovers of the great outdoors such as walkers and cyclists. Isaac's Tea Trail passes through the site, directly on the C2C and with bicycle hire (including electric bikes) available nearby. Pre-booked breakfast and evening meals can be provided for larger groups. The campsite has tiered pitches to enhance the views across the Nent valley. Electric hook-ups available in the car park.

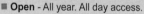
DETAILS

- **Open** - All year. All day access.
- **Beds** - 25: 1x4/5, 1x9, 1x11
- **Price/night** - £20pp. Sole use £400, £1080 (3 nights). Camping: £12, U15, £7. Motorhomes/caravans £25 up to 2.

CONTACT: Danny Taylor
Tel: 07919 092403/ 01434 382486
info@haggsbank.com
haggsbank.com
Haggs Bank Bunkhouse, Nentsbury,
Alston, Cumbria, CA9 3LH

NINEBANKS
YOUTH HOSTEL

Book a bed, a room, a chalet room or the whole hostel. Ninebanks 4* Hostel, in stunning rural Northumberland, has en-suite bedrooms, a sitting room with log-burner and a spacious dining room. In the chalet are two high quality studio rooms, fully self-contained and separate from the hostel. Dogs welcome with prior notice for sole use or in the chalet. In the North Pennines close to Hadrian's Wall and on Isaac's Tea Trail.

DETAILS
- **Open** - All year. All day. Office 5-10pm.
- **Beds** - Hostel 28: 2x2/3, 2x4, 1x6, 1x8. Chalets 1 x double, 1 x double plus bunk.
- **Price/night** - Beds from £17, rooms from £39, whole hostel from £200. Chalet from £60. Dogs incur a cleaning fee

CONTACT: Pauline or Ian
Tel: 01434 345288
contact@ninebanks.com
www.ninebanks.org.uk
Orchard House, Mohope, Hexham,
Northumberland NE47 8DQ

ALSTON
YOUTH HOSTEL

On the very eastern edge of Cumbria, nestled in the North Pennines and within the historic town of Alston, is Alston Youth Hostel. Not only is the hostel about halfway on the very popular Coast to Coast (C2C) cycle route but it is also located directly on the Pennine Way. The perfect stop-over for walkers and cyclists. You'll receive a warm welcome, We're also available for exclusive hire!

DETAILS

- **Open** - All year, 8am-10am, 5pm-10pm
- **Beds** - 30: 2x2, 2x4, 3x6
- **Price/night** - From £23pp. Private rooms from £45. Discount of up to 15% for YHA/IH members. Sole use from £550 for 2 nights midweek, £690 for 2 nights Fri-Sat.

CONTACT: Linda or Neil Willmott
Tel: 01434 381509
alston@yha.org.uk
alstonyouthhostel.co.uk
Firs Edge, The Firs, Alston, Cumbria,
CA9 3RW

CARRSHIELD
CAMPING BARN
205

Surrounded by the fells & valleys of the North Pennines, Carrshield Camping Barn offers basic accommodation for 18 across 3 rooms, each with a wood-burner and a wooden sleeping platform. There's a separate cooking area & a composting WC. BYO stove, utensils & sleeping bag/mat. Perfectly located it's on the Isaac's Tea Trail, C2C cycle route and close to a number of mountain bike routes. Camping may be available.

DETAILS
- **Open** - All year. Check in 3pm, check out 10am
- **Beds -** 18: 1x8, 1x6, 1x4
- **Price/night** - 8 person room: £45, 6 person room: £35, 4 person room £25. Prices includes a basket of logs per room.

CONTACT: Kim Emmerson
Tel: 01434 345913
barneycraig.avel@gmail.com
www.carrshieldcampingbarn.co.uk
Near Blue Row Cottages, Carrshield, Hexham, NE47 8AR

GARRIGILL
VILLAGE HALL
206a

ALLENHEADS
LODGE
206b

Perfect for the Pennine Way or C2C cycle route. In the lovely village of Garrigill, the bunkroom above the village hall sleeps 8 with bedding hire available. Larger groups can BYO bedding and use the hall itself where 12 camp beds are available. There is free WiFi, a well equipped kitchen, showers and drying room. It makes the ideal long distance walk/C2C stop over.

Situated in the heart of the North Pennines, Allenheads Lodge is an excellent venue for outdoor activities or relaxing in the peaceful countryside. An ideal accommodation stop on the C2C cycle route it's just 47 miles from the North Sea coast. Comfortable and well equipped, the lodge has 24 beds in four rooms, central heating, individual toilet and showers and a large kitchen/dining room. The lodge also boasts hot showers, drying facilities, bed linen and secure bike storage.

DETAILS
- **Open** - All year. All day
- **Beds** - 35: Bunkroom: 8 bunks. Main Hall: 12 camp beds + floor space for 15.
- **Price/night** - £15pp. Bunkroom bedding hire (if required) £5 pp per stay. Camping £7 pp (£4 DofE or other youth activity groups).

DETAILS
- **Open** - All year. All day.
- **Beds** - 24
- **Price/night** - Bed only: £19.50pp. B&B: £25pp. Ask for group discounts.

CONTACT: Bookings Secretary
Tel: 01434 647516
bookings@garrigillvh.org
www.garrigillvh.org.uk
Garrigill Village Hall, Garrigill, Alston, Cumbria, CA9 3DS

CONTACT: Andrea Cowie
Tel: 01915 155300
acowie@springboard-ne.org
allenheadslodge.com
Allenheads Lodge, Allenheads, Northumberland NE47 9HW

BARRINGTON
BUNKHOUSE
207a

CARRS FARM
BUNKHOUSE
207b

Situated in the peaceful village of Rookhope, in Weardale, Barrington Bunkhouse accommodates 15 people. There's room for 13 in the bunkhouse, whilst the adjacent caravan sleeps two. Camping space is also available.

The kitchen is equipped with two toasters, a kettle, a microwave and a fridge, whilst The Rookhope Inn next door serves fine food. All are welcome; cyclists, walkers and family groups.

Carrs Farm Bunkhouse is a converted 17th century barn with stunning views over Weardale. It provides comfortable bunk bed accommodation for groups of up to 21 people, in three rooms.

There is a fully equipped self catering kitchen, games/lounge area and outdoor seating with BBQ. Situated on a working farm at the heart of the North Pennines. Guided walks and outdoor activities are available for groups and schools.

DETAILS

- **Open** - All year, All day.
- **Beds** - 12 (+1): 1 x 12 + 1 fold up bed
- **Price/night** - £24pp incl. snack b/fast. Camping £14 with b/fast, £10 without. Sole use rates negotiable.

DETAILS

- **Open** - All year (Arrival time: from 4pm. Departure time: before 10am)
- **Beds** - 21: 2x6, 1x9
- **Price/night** - £20 per person. Enquire about sole use.

CONTACT: Valerie Livingston
Tel: 01388 517656
barrington_bunkhouse@hotmail.co.uk
www.barrington-bunkhouse-rookhope.com
Barrington Cottage, Rookhope,
Weardale, Co. Durham, DL13 2BG

CONTACT: Joy Henderson
Tel: 07592 744 649
joy.henderson@carrsfarm.co.uk
carrsfarm.co.uk
Carrs Farm, Wolsingham, County
Durham, DL13 3BQ

EDMUNDBYERS YHA
LOW HOUSE HAVEN
208

Edmunbyers hostel lies in moorland, close to the Northumberland/County Durham boundary, with fine views. It's just two miles from Derwent Reservoir, for sailing & fishing. Ideal for walking holidays, it's also on the C2C cycle route & is close to Hadrian's Wall & Beamish outdoor museum. Cosy & comfortable with optional home cooked evening meals & breakfasts.

DETAILS
- **Open** - All year (camping Apr-Oct). Check in 5-10pm, check out 8-10am.
- **Beds** - 31: 1x8, 1x6, 2x5, 1x4, 1x3 plus 14 camping pitches (6 with electric)
- **Price/night** - From £23 (adult), £19 (under 18). Discounts for YHA members: Room for 3:£60, 4:£70, 5:£80, 6:£90.

CONTACT: Debbie Clarke
Tel: 01207 255651 Mob: 07884 969725
info@lowhousehaven.co.uk
www.lowhousehaven.co.uk
Low House, Edmundbyers, Consett, Durham, DH8 9NL

ALLENDALE
BUNKHOUSE
209a

DENEHOLME
209b

Allendale Bunkhouse sits on the Market Square overlooking the hustle and bustle of this small country town, the fells & River East Allen beyond. It is an oasis for walkers, cyclists, horse riders, families, groups of friends and youth & school groups alike.

Book a bunk, a room, a floor (up to 18) or the whole bunkhouse (up to 39). Allendale is well served with tea rooms, the Forge art gallery & café, a quirky gift shop, a pharmacy, and three wonderful country pubs, all serving food and all family & dog friendly.

On the edge of Allendale, in the North Pennines AONB, Deneholme hostel & outdoor activity centre accommodates groups of 14-40. Perfect for schools, clubs, family reunions & weddings. Stag/ hen groups are welcome. Self cater or catered. This impressive Edwardian country house set in expansive lawns and 5 acres of steep woodland has 11 bedrooms and plenty of communal areas, some large enough for 40+ guests to dine/celebrate together.

DETAILS

- **Open** - All year.
- **Beds** - 42: 1x8,1x6,5x4,1x3,2x2,1x1
- **Price/night** - Depends on group size, time of year, length of stay, catering & activities. From £90pp for a w/end.

DETAILS

- **Open** - All year. 8am-8pm.
- **Beds** - 39: 1x1,1x3, 2x4, 1x5, 2x6, 1x8
- **Price/night** - From £14 - £40pp.

CONTACT: Linda Beck
Tel: 01434 618579
info@allendalebunkhouse.co.uk
allendalebunkhouse.co.uk
Market Place, Allendale, Hexham,
NE47 9BD

CONTACT: Linda Beck
Tel: 01434 618579 / 07791707097
linda@n-a-c.co.uk
deneholme.com
Deneholme, Allendale, Hexham,
Northumberland, NE47 9PX

BIRDOSWALD
BUNKHOUSE
210

Birdoswald Bunkhouse is a 17th century farmhouse built into the remains of Birdoswald Roman Fort on the best preserved stretch of Hadrian's Wall. Set within an English Heritage estate, the bunkhouse is an ideal base for wild walks with breathtaking views and discovering the area's Roman heritage. The bunkhouse provides group accommodation for groups of between 15 and 37 people, with seven bedrooms, a large farmhouse kitchen and a dining room with views over the fort.

       **GROUPS ONLY**

DETAILS
- **Open** - All year
- **Beds** - 37 in 7 rooms
- **Price/night** - Enquire for prices. Minimum group size of 15.

CONTACT: Reservations team
Tel: 03703 331187
accommodation@english-heritage.org.uk
www.english-heritage.org.uk
Birdoswald Roman Fort, Gilsland,
Brampton, Cumbria, CA8 7DD

SLACK HOUSE
FARM

Slack House Farm is a working, organic farm overlooking Birdoswald Roman Fort on Hadrian's Wall. On the NCN 72 cycle trail and bordering the dark skies of Kielder and the Northumberland National Park. Half a km from Hadrian's Wall National Trail. The bunkbarn is adjacent to the farm's cheese dairy. It is heated and has basic self-catering facilities and an outdoor cooking/barbecue cabin. Breakfasts, farmhouse suppers, ready meals and packed lunches available.

DETAILS

- **Open** - All year. Check in from 5pm (4pm GMT), check out by 10am.
- **Beds** - 18: 1x10, 1x5, 1x3 (family)
- **Price/night** - Beds £15pp. Sole use: 5 bed room £60, family £45, Camp-loft £80.

CONTACT: Dianne Horn
Tel: 01697 747351 or 07900 472342
slackhouseorganicfarm@gmail.com
slackhousefarm.co.uk
Slack House Farm, Gilsland Brampton,
Cumbria, CA8 7DB

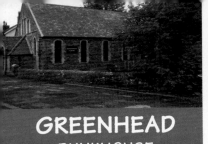

GREENHEAD
BUNKHOUSE
212a

FLORRIE'S
BUNKHOUSE
212b

Situated in the village of Greenhead on both the Pennine Way and Hadrian's Wall, the bunkhouse is ideal for walking the Pennine Way Trail or The Wall Path or for exploring the nearby Roman heritage sites. It has a self-catering kitchen big enough for large groups. The flexible accommodation can be booked by the bed, the room or for sole use. Greenhead hostel/ bunkhouse is run by Greenhead Hotel just over the road.

Located right on the Hadrian's Wall National Trail this newly converted bunkhouse is aimed at walkers or cyclists. With drying room and cycle storage this is the perfect stop-over on the trail. Open for individuals from April to October, Florrie's provides a comfortable bed, breakfast and evening meals plus the opportunity to socialise with other guests at the bar. From October 2020 the bunkhouse will be open to groups in the winter season with self-catering.

DETAILS

- **Open** - March to September. Please enquire for availability throughout winter.
- **Beds** - 45: Hostel 40: 2x8 4x6. Flat 5: 2dbl,1 single.
- **Price/night** - Bunkhouse: From £16pp, sole use £600. Flat (sleeps 5) £90.

DETAILS

- **Open** - April to October. (Sole use for groups available in the winter season).
- **Beds** - 16 (17) : 3x4, 1x4 (or 5 if family)
- **Price/night** - B&B £25pp. Private rooms available. Ask for group rates.

CONTACT: Greenhead Hotel
Tel: 01697 747411
enquiries@greenheadhotelandhostel.co.uk
greenheadhotel.com
Greenhead Hotel, Greenhead,
Brampton, Cumbria, CA8 7HG

CONTACT: Rebecca & Joss
Tel: 01697 741704
hello@florriesonthewall.co.uk
florriesonthewall.co.uk
Florrie's on the Wall, Kingbank, Walton,
Cumbria, CA8 2DH

GIBBS HILL
FARM HOSTEL

213

Gibbs Hill Farm Hostel is on a working hill farm near Once Brewed and Hadrian's Wall and close to the Pennine Way. Designed to reduce energy consumption it is centrally heated throughout. Comprising 3 bunkrooms, 2 shower rooms, 2 toilets, a well equipped kitchen, a comfortable communal area and a large deck where you can enjoy the evening sun. Ideal for families who can book a whole room with private facilities. Study groups welcome. Self catering only.

DETAILS
- **Open** - All year
- **Beds** - 18: 3x6
- **Price/night** - £18 adult, £12 child (under 12), including bedding.

CONTACT: Valerie Gibson
Tel: 01434 344030
val@gibbshillfarm.co.uk
www.gibbshillfarm.co.uk
Gibbs Hill Farm, Bardon Mill, Nr
Hexham, Northumberland, NE47 7AP

NEWBROUGH
BUNKHOUSE
214

In the centre of the village of Newbrough, this community run bunkhouse sleeps 22 across 3 dorms. Facilities include 2 shower/WC rooms, 2 sink areas & a small equipped kitchen. A large communal area is available to groups by arrangement. With footpaths leading directly to Hadrian's Wall, approx 3 miles away, it is popular with walkers. While for cyclists the Sandstone Way & Hadrian's Cycleway pass right by.

DETAILS

- **Open** - All year. Check in 3pm. Check out before 10am.
- **Beds** - 22: 2x8, 1x6
- **Price/night** - £24pp (incl bedding). 6 bed room £90, 8 bed room £118. Whole bunkhouse £292 (bedding £6pp per stay).

CONTACT: Nick Springham
Tel: 07707 778094, 07533 356443.
info@newbroughbunkhouse.co.uk
www.newbroughbunkhouse.co.uk
The Stanegate, Newbrough, Hexham, Northumberland, NE47 5AR

DEMESNE FARM
BUNKHOUSE
215a

BROWN RIGG
GUEST ROOMS
215b

This bunkhouse is on a working hill farm in the centre of Bellingham and near to Northumberland National Park. Situated on the Pennine Way, Route 68 and the Reivers & Sandstone Way cycle routes, it is an ideal base for exploring Northumberland, Hadrian's Wall, Kielder Water and many climbing crags. The bunkhouse is very well appointed with quality bunks, a well equipped kitchen, a farmhouse table to seat 15 and a large comfortable communal area.

Brown Rigg Guest Rooms offer luxury hostel accommodation in the Northumberland National Park. Close to Bellingham, for Kielder Water & Forest Park, it is also directly on the Pennine Way & 400m to the Sandstone Way, Reviers Route & Pennine Cycleway. The 6 double guest rooms can be booked alongside the 4 lodges. A function hall & outdoor activities are available on site.

DETAILS

■ **Open** - All year. Hours flexible but no check in after 9pm.
■ **Beds** - 15: 1x8, 1x4, 1x3.
■ **Price/night** - £22 per person, £16 under 18's (including linen).

CONTACT: Robert Telfer
Tel: 07967 396345
stay@demesnefarmcampsite.co.uk
www.demesnefarmcampsite.co.uk
Demesne Farm, Bellingham, Hexham, Northumberland, NE48 2BS

DETAILS

■ **Open** - All year. Check in 3-9pm. Check out by 10am.
■ **Beds** - 12: 6x2 (2 singles or 1 double). Plus Lodges 24: 4x6
■ **Price/night** - Guest Rooms: £50-£60 per room (2 people). £40-£50 single occupancy. Continental breakfast box £5.

CONTACT: Sue & Alastair Hunter
Tel: 01434 220390
guestrooms@brownrigglodges.com
www.brownrigglodges.com
Brown Rigg, Bellingham, Northumberland. NE48 2HR

HOUGHTON NORTH

FARM ACCOMMODATION

216

Houghton North Farm, partly built with stones from Hadrian's Wall is in the beautiful Northumberland countryside right on the Hadrian's Wall trail, 15 miles from the start. This spacious new build is perfect for groups, individuals or families. The bunkrooms are located around the central courtyard. There is a self-catering kitchen (continental breakfast included). The TV lounge has a log fire and WiFi. Long-term parking, baggage transfer and packed lunches are available on request.

DETAILS

- **Open** - All year. Arrive after 3.30pm depart by 10am.
- **Beds** - 22: 1x5, 3x4, 1x3, 1x2.
- **Price/night** - B&B from £25-£40 (adult) Group discounts.

CONTACT: Mrs Paula Laws
Tel: 01661 854364
wjlaws@btconnect.com
www.houghtonnorthfarm.co.uk
Houghton North Farm, Heddon-on-the-Wall, Northumberland, NE15 0EZ

GIBSIDE
STABLES
217

This grade II listed stable block on the National Trust Gibside Estate is now a comfortable, well equipped bunkhouse sleeping 37 in 4 rooms, or 18 in 2 rooms. Up to 3 dogs welcomed by arrangement. Enjoy the cafés & activities on the estate during the day & have the whole park to yourselves in the evening. Within driving distance of the Northumberland coast, Newcastle, Durham, NT Cragside, NT Wallington & NT Souter Lighthouse.

      GROUPS ONLY

DETAILS
- **Open** - All year. All day
- **Beds** - 37: 1x16, 1x17, 2x2
- **Price/night** - From £525 for (min) 2 nights for half the bunkhouse (sleeps 18). £1050 for (min) 2 nights for the full bunkhouse (sleeps 37).

CONTACT: National Trust Holidays
Tel: 03443 351296
bunkhouses@nationaltrust.org.uk
www.nationaltrust.org.uk/holidays
Nr Rowlands Gill, Gateshead, Tyne & Wear, NE16 6BG

TARSET TOR

BUNKHOUSE & BOTHIES

218

In the heart of the Northumberland International Dark Sky Park and close to the Pennine Way. These striking timber eco-buildings integrate into their natural surroundings making the most of this remarkable location and providing the perfect base for outdoor adventures.

The bunkhouse and bothies provide stylish, versatile & comfortable self-catering accommodation which can be used for events, conferences & parties.

DETAILS

- **Open** - Mid January - December.
- **Beds** - 44: Bunkhouse:16-20. Bothies: 4x8. 3 camper van bays.
- **Price/night** - Bunkhouse: £180 to £440. Bothies: £90 to £250.

CONTACT: Robert and Claire Cocker
Tel: 01434 240980
info@tarset-tor.co.uk
www.tarset-tor.co.uk
Greystones, Lanehead, Tarset, Hexham,
NE48 1NT

WALLINGTON
BUNKHOUSE
219

Situated in the heart of the National Trust Wallington Estate, visitors to the bunkhouse will have free access to the mansion, it's shops and café. Perfect for groups of families with lots of on-site activities including cycling and play areas or for walkers wanting a base from which to visit the Cheviots and Hadrian's wall, both within an hour's drive.

The bunkhouse is perfect for self-catering groups with a large well-equipped kitchen and large living/dining area. It sleeps 20 in four rooms.

       GROUPS ONLY

DETAILS
- **Open** - All year. All day.
- **Beds** - 20: 2x8, 2x2
- **Price/night** - From £400 for two nights.

CONTACT: National Trust Holidays
Tel: 0344 335 1296
bunkhouses@nationaltrust.org.uk
www.nationaltrust.org.uk/holidays
Wallington, Cambo, Morpeth,
Northumberland, NE61 4AR

CHARTNERS FARM
OFF THE GRID
220

Hidden away in the heart of Harwood Forest, 20 miles NW of Morpeth, Chartners Farm is definitely off the grid. It's a 5 mile drive along forest tracks from the road. All electricity is generated by wind turbines & solar panels, while a huge log burner heats the radiators and keeps the place at a cosy 20 degrees. The perfect spot to escape the rat race, unwind & recharge. With no WiFi you can really switch off! Nature surrounds you. Come & enjoy complete peace and tranquility.

      **GROUPS ONLY**

DETAILS

■ **Open** - All year. Check in after 1pm. Check out before 11am
■ **Beds** - 12: 2x5,1x2 (bunks and singles)
■ **Price/night** - £95 sole use. Minimum stay 2 nights.

CONTACT: Paul Kirkpatrick
Tel: 07867 795586
paul@off-the-grid-cic.uk
Harwood Forest, Ewesley, Morpeth
NE61 4LJ

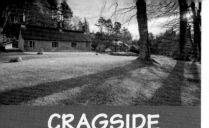

CRAGSIDE
BUNKHOUSE

221

A traditional conversion of Victorian workers' cottages in the centre of the National Trust Cragside Estate with fabulous views overlooking the lake.

Cragside bunkhouse sleeps 16 in 5 rooms with a well equipped self-catering kitchen, making it the perfect base for families or other groups wanting to explore this stunning part of the UK. Located in the heart of Northumberland, an hour's drive to the coast, the Cheviots and Hadrian's Wall.

       GROUPS ONLY

DETAILS

- **Open** - All year. All day
- **Beds** - 16: 1x6, 1x4, 3x2
- **Price/night** - Sole use: 2 nights from £380.

CONTACT: National Trust Holidays
Tel: 03443 351296
bunkhouses@nationaltrust.org.uk
www.nationaltrust.org.uk/holidays
Cragside, Rothbury, Morpeth,
Northumberland, NE65 7PX

ALNWICK
YOUTH HOSTEL

This family friendly 4* hostel has en suite rooms, cosy lounge, games room and a spacious dining room. Located in the centre of town, it is ideal for Alnwick Castle, (of Downton Abbey and Harry Potter fame) and Alnwick Garden. The coast, with castles at Dunstanburgh and Bamburgh, Farne Isles, magical Holy Island and glorious sandy beaches is just a 15 minute drive. While inland the Cheviot Hills & Hadrian's Wall await you.

DETAILS

- **Open** - All year. 8-10am, 4-7pm
- **Beds** - 56: 1xdbl,2x2,1x3,6x4,1x5,3x6
- **Price/night** - Peak season: dorm £25. 2 bedded rooms £60. 4 bedded rooms £80. Off-peak: dorm £18. 2 bedded rooms £40. 4 bedded rooms £40.

CONTACT: Lindsay McFarlane
Tel: 01665 660800
info@alnwickyouthhostel.co.uk
www.alnwickyouthhostel.co.uk
34 - 38 Green Batt, Alnwick,
Northumberland, NE66 1TU

ALBATROSS
HOSTEL
223

Fly high with the award winning "Albatross"! This clean and modern hostel is located in Newcastle's city centre. Providing rooms from 2 bed to 12 beds and anything in between for as little as £17. The overnight price includes; linen, 24hr reception, fully fitted self-catering kitchen with free tea, coffee and toast, free WiFi access and computer terminals, pool table, satellite TV, free baggage storage and chargeable laundry facilities. The Albatross offers the perfect city centre base for international travellers, walkers, cyclists, and bikers.

DETAILS

- **Open** - All year. All day.
- **Beds** - 176
- **Price/night** - From £17pp (dorm).

CONTACT: Reception
Tel: 0191 2331330
info@albatrossnewcastle.co.uk
albatrossnewcastle.co.uk
51 Grainger Street, Newcastle upon Tyne, NE1 5JE

MOUNTHOOLY
BUNKHOUSE

224

Nestled in the beautiful College Valley, North Northumberland, Mounthooly Bunkhouse is a perfect stop-off on the Pennine Way and St Cuthbert's Way. Dogs are welcome by arrangement. There is a well equipped kitchen and living area with log burner. Bedding is supplied. Cars need a permit to access the private valley which is provided on arrival. A haven for wildlife with red squirrels, otters and a thriving population of feral goats in the valley. The perfect wild get away from it all.

DETAILS
- **Open** - All year. All day.
- **Beds** - 24: 2x9 1x2 1x4
- **Price/night** - £18ppn. Discount for concessions and sole use.

CONTACT: Charlene Drysdale
Tel: 01668 216210
mounthooly@college-valley.co.uk
www.college-valley.co.uk
Mount Hooley, College Valley, Wooler,
Northumberland, NE71 6TU

ILDERTON
DOD BARNS

Ilderton Dod Barns are a luxury bunkhouse & a self-contained cottage in the Northumberland National Park. On a working hill farm down a 1.5 mile private track, the former stables have been restored to provide quality, cosy accommodation. Ideally located close to The Pennine Way, The Sandstone Way & with many other footpaths & bridleways on the doorstep. The perfect base for walkers, mountain bikers and horse riders (paddocks available).

DETAILS

- **Open** - All year.
- **Beds** - 8 in The Barn plus 2/3 in Cuckoo Cottage
- **Price/night** - The Barn: £308-£514 for a 3 night weekend. £410-£685 per week.

CONTACT: Mrs Margaret Brown
Tel: 01668 281745
mbrownatcoldmartin@hotmail.co.uk
www.ildertondodbarns.co.uk
Ilderton, Wooler, Northumberland
NE66 4JL

WOOLER
YOUTH HOSTEL
226

Wooler Youth Hostel & Shepherd's Huts are on the edge of the town and offer an ideal base for exploring the Northumberland National Park, the Cheviot Hills, local castles and fine sandy beaches. For walkers there's St Cuthbert's Way and for cyclists, Wooler cycle hub routes, Pennine Cycleway and the Sandstone Way. There are bridleways perfect for mountain biking and lots of bouldering and climbing.

DETAILS

- **Open** - March-Oct. (Group bookings Nov to Feb). Reception 8-10am & 5-9pm.
- **Beds** - 53: 3x2, 6x4, 1x6, 1x8. Shepherd's huts 3x2, 1x3 (family).
- **Price/night** - From £22 adult, £20 child. Group discounts available.

CONTACT: Hostel Manager
Tel: 01668 281365
info@woolerhostel.co.uk
www.woolerhostel.co.uk
30 Cheviot Street, Wooler,
Northumberland, NE71 6LW

CHATTON PARK
BUNKHOUSE
227a

A former smithy converted into a self-catering bunkhouse on a mixed working farm.1/2 mile from Chatto, 8 miles from Northumberland's vast empty beaches and historic castles and 5 miles from the heather clad Cheviot Hills. Walking, water sports, climbing, fishing, golf and cycling are all nearby. The 2 dorms can be rented separately. There is a fully equipped kitchen, seating around the original blacksmith's fire & hot showers.

DETAILS
- **Open** - March to November. Flexible times but no check in after 9pm.
- **Beds** - 12: 2x6.
- **Price/night** - From £15. Group rates available. Teens must be led by a responsible adult. Dogs: £10/dog/stay.

CONTACT: Jane or Duncan
Tel: 01668 215765 or 01668 215247
jaord@btinternet.com
www.chattonparkfarm.co.uk
Chatton Park Farm, Chatton, Alnwick, Northumberland, NE66 5RA

BLUEBELL
FARM BUNKBARN
227b

Bluebell Farm Bunkbarn is within walking distance of shops and pubs. It is ideally located for exploring Nothumberland's Heritage Coast, the Cheviot Hills and the Scottish Borders. The Bunkbarn sleeps 14, the Studio 4. Plus 2 studio apartments and 5 self-catering cottages. There is a shared modern toilet block. BYO sleeping bags/towels or hire. Studio apartments & cottages have bed linen.

DETAILS
- **Open** - All year. Check in by 9 pm, departure by 10 am.
- **Beds** - Bunkbarn 14: 1x8, 1x6. Studio 4: 1x4.
- **Price/night** - Bunkbarn: £15 under 16s £8. Studio: £20 under 16s £10. Linen and towel hire £8pp. Sole use rates available.

CONTACT: Phyl
Tel: 01668 213362
corillas@icloud.com
www.bluebellfarmbelford.com
Bluebell Farm Caravan Park, Belford, Northumberland, NE70 7QE

THE HIDES

Located in Seahouses with an easy walk to St Aidan's beach. The Hides provide affordable accommodation on the magnificent Northumbrian Coast.

Perfect for groups, families or independent travellers. Each Hide is an en-suite room sleeping 4 in beds & bunks. The rooms open onto a communal courtyard with access to the well equipped, self-catering kitchen, bike storage, drying room & laundry.

DETAILS

- **Open** - All year.
- **Beds** - 20: 5x4
- **Price/night** - £25. Children £22. Minimum 2 night stay. Bedding hire £5. Dogs £5

CONTACT: Kerry
Tel: 01665 720645
info@the-hides.co.uk
www.the-hides.co.uk
146 Main Street, Seahouses
Northumberland NE68 7UA

SEAHOUSES
HOSTEL
229

Within easy walking distance of Seahouses, this recently refurbished hostel offers affordable, spacious & comfortable accommodation. A perfect base for visiting the beaches and castles of the Northumbrian Coast. Particularly popular with divers, families, cyclists, walkers, school, church and youth groups, parties of all sizes welcome, sole use also available. Booking is essential.

DETAILS

- **Open** - All year. Arrive after 4pm, depart by 10am unless otherwise agreed.
- **Beds** - 42: 1x8, 2×2 (en-suite), 1x6 (en-suite wet room), 2x4, 1x6, 1×10
- **Price/night** - £20-£26pp. Children, recognised youth groups & leaders £17pp. Under 5s free. Min 2 nights.

CONTACT: Karen Leadbitter
Tel: 07531 305206
seahouseshostel@outlook.com
www.seahouseshostel.org.uk
157 Main Street, Seahouses,
Northumberland NE68 7TU

SPRINGHILL
BUNKHOUSE

Springhill's Lookout & Wigwams offer great value, comfortable accommodation which can be booked as a whole or on a per bed/night basis. Ideal for groups, families or couples. Superbly located on the Northumberland Heritage Coastline there are stunning views towards the Farne Islands and Cheviot Hills while Seahouses and Bamburgh are within very easy reach.

DETAILS

■ **Open** - All year. Arrive 3-6pm, departure by 10am. Cleaning noon-4pm.
■ **Beds** - The Lookout 32: 8x4. Wigwams 40: 5x8. Wigwam Ensuite 8: 2x4.
■ **Price/night** - The Lookout £480 sole use per night. Wigwams £21.50 pppn. En-suite Wigwams £27.50 pppn.

CONTACT: Springhill Accommodation
Tel: 07753 856895
enquiries@springhill-farm.co.uk
www.springhill-farm.co.uk
Springhill Farm, Seahouses,
Northumberland NE68 7UR

JOINERS SHOP
BUNKHOUSE
231a

MAUGHOLD
VENTURE CENTRE
231b

Nestled in the hamlet of Preston, The Joiners Shop Bunkhouse is just 5 miles from the Northumberland coastline & 7 miles from Alnwick famed for its (Harry Potter) castle & gardens.

The charming 19th century building sleeps 18 in heated sections of 2s, 3s & a 5. Fully equipped kitchen, spacious dining area, lounge with fire & hot showers. Close to NCN Route 1.

Maughold Venture Centre Bunkhouse overlooks farmland with views out to sea. The popular beach of Port e Vullen is just 10 min's walk away. Enjoy self-catering accommodation, with en suite, centrally heated rooms. Tasty meals are available from the neighbouring Venture Centre, where you can also book kayaking, abseiling, air rifle shooting, archery, gorge walking, dinghy sailing & team events. With its own stop, Lewaigue Halt, on the Manx Electric Railway you have easy access to Douglas, Ramsey, mountains & tranquil glens.

DETAILS

- **Open** - All year. All day. Must confirm time before arriving.
- **Beds** - 18
- **Price/night** - £15 pp. Sole use £150-£270 depending on numbers.

DETAILS

- **Open** - January - December. 24 hours.
- **Beds** - 52: 2x2, 1x5, 4x8, 2x10.
- **Price/night** - £12-£15 per person.

CONTACT: Kirsten Sutherland
Tel: 01665 589135 or 07955 230328
thejoinersshop.bunkhouse@outlook.com
www.bunkhousenorthumberland.co.uk
Preston, Chathill, Northumberland
NE67 5ES

CONTACT: Simon Read
Tel: 01624 814240
contact@adventure-centre.co.uk
www.venturecentre.im
The Venture Centre, Maughold,
Isle of Man, IM7 1AW

KNOCKALOE BEG

FARM BUNKHOUSE
232

A working farm nestled under Peel Hill, Isle of Man, Knockaloe Beg offers B&B, cottages, bunkhouse, bothy & glamping. The bunkhouse sleeps 10 in two rooms. There's a central communal area with log burner, dining table, TV/DVD & comfy settees. The bothy is a cosy, twin bed room. Washing facilities are a short step outside. In the orchard there are two deluxe, en suite glamping cabins each sleeping four.

DETAILS
- **Open** - All year
- **Beds** - 20: Bunkhouse 10: 1x7, 1x3. Bothy 2. Cabins 8: 2x4
- **Price/night** - Bunkhouse - £20 pp (£15 single night supplement). Bothy - £25 pp (£15 single night supplement). Breakfast (when available) £12.

CONTACT: Fiona and John Anderson
Tel: 01624 844279
info@knockaloebegfarm.com
www.knockaloebegfarm.com
Patrick, Isle of Man, IM5 3AQ

CASTLE WARD
BUNKHOUSE

233

This traditional Bunkhouse is the perfect base to explore the stunning gardens, visit the beautiful shores of Stangford Lough or take the ferry to Portaferry. Sleeping up to 14 in three upstairs rooms, it is a great choice for groups & family get-togethers. The estate has walking, cycle trails plus play areas making this a particularly family friendly spot. It is also a huge hit for Game of Thrones fans as the original Castle Ward was the location for 'Winterfell'. The retail shop has tons of brilliant HBO GOT memorabilia.

DETAILS

- **Open** - All year
- **Beds** - 14: 2x6, 1x2
- **Price/night** - 2 nights from £320

CONTACT: National Trust Holidays
Tel: 03448 002070
bunkhouses@nationaltrust.org.uk
www.nationaltrust.org.uk/holidays
National Trust Castle Ward, Strangford,
Co Down, Northern Ireland, BT30 7LS

South Wales

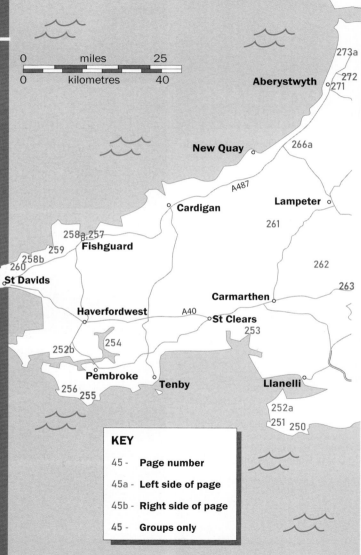

0 — miles — 25
0 — kilometres — 40

273a
272
271
Aberystwyth

New Quay

266a

A487

Cardigan

Lampeter

261

258a, 257
259
Fishguard

258b
260
St Davids

262

263

Carmarthen

Haverfordwest

A40

St Clears

253

252b
254

256 255
Pembroke
Tenby

Llanelli

252a
251 250

KEY

45 - **Page number**

45a - **Left side of page**

45b - **Right side of page**

45 - **Groups only**

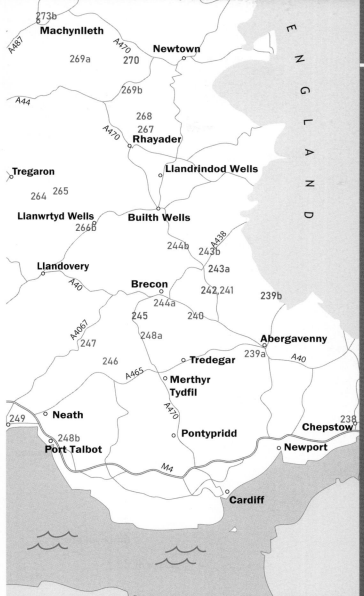

South Wales

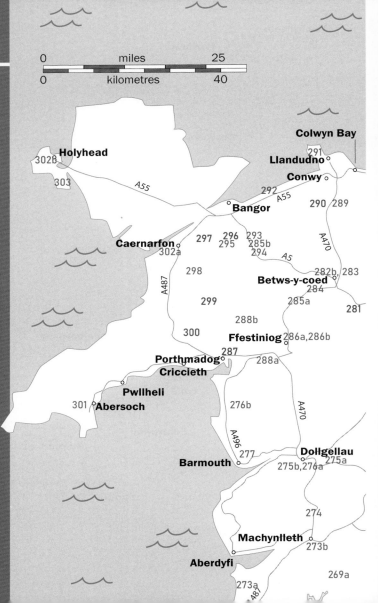

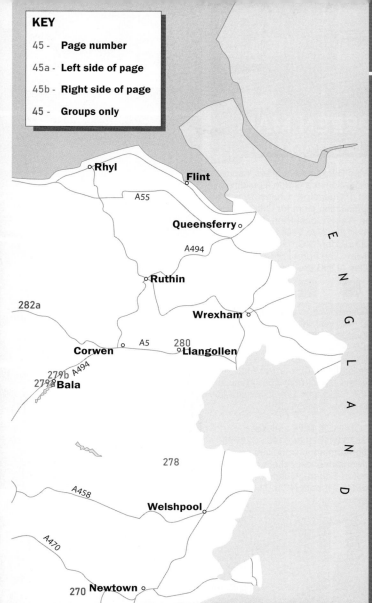

KEY

45 - **Page number**

45a - **Left side of page**

45b - **Right side of page**

45 - **Groups only**

Rhyl

Flint

Queensferry

A55

A494

Ruthin

282a

Wrexham

Corwen   A5   280 Llangollen

279b A494
279a Bala

278

A458

Welshpool

A470

270 Newtown

ENGLAND

North Wales

GREEN MAN
BACKPACKERS

Green Man Backpackers offers inspired accommodation in a Grade II building in the heart of Chepstow. Chepstow is the starting/finishing point for Offa's Dyke path, the Wales Coast Path, Gloucester Way and the Wye Valley Walk. The Land's End/John O'Groats route is just 1 mile away. The Forest of Dean & Wye Valley AONB are also nearby.

DETAILS

■ **Open** - All year. All day. Except New Year's Eve/Day.

■ **Beds** - 49: 28 in dorms of 6 or 4 beds, 5 en suite family / twin rooms.

■ **Price/night** - Dorms from £22pp, family/4 bed rooms from £65 (en suite from £75), 5 bed from £75, family/double en suite (sleeps 3) from £55.

CONTACT: Mick and Ness
Tel: 07870 611979 or 01291 626773
info@greenmanbackpackers.co.uk
greenmanbackpackers.co.uk
13 Beaufort Square, Chepstow, NP16 5EP (Car park NP16 5LL)

MIDDLE NINFA
BUNKHOUSE
239a

THE WAIN HOUSE
239b

Middle Ninfa Farm, on the edge of the Blaenavon World Heritage Site in the Brecon Beacons, offers bunkhouse/cottage accommodation, camping on eleven 'remote' pitches and hands-on training in coracle making and willow sculpture. Sympathetically renovated to retain the rustic charm with fine views over the Usk Valley, the bunkhouse provides comfortable self-catering accommodation for up to 6 people. BYO food, sleeping bags, & pillowcases.

This old stone barn continues the tradition of 900 years when Llanthony Priory next door provided accommodation. Surrounded by the Black Mountains in the Brecon Beacons National Park, it is your ideal base for all mountain activities. There is a fully equipped kitchen, hot showers, heating throughout and a wood burning stove. Small or large groups are welcome with sole use and a minimum charge. Two pubs nearby offer real ale and bar food.

DETAILS
- **Open** - All year.
- **Beds** - 6: 1x4, 1x2 (dbl) plus camping.
- **Price/night** - From £10pp. Weekly rate for 6 persons £300-360. Camping (inc hammocks) £5 pp + pitch fee of £5/£10.

DETAILS
- **Open** - All year. All day. No restrictions.
- **Beds** - 16: 1x8, 1x4, 1x6.
- **Price/night** - £35 per person for a two-night weekend, with a minimum charge of £350. Mid-week reductions

CONTACT: Richard and Rohan Lewis
Tel: 01873 854662
bookings@middleninfa.co.uk
www.middleninfa.co.uk
Middle Ninfa Farm, Llanellen, Abergavenny, NP7 9LE

CONTACT: Cordelia Passmore
Tel: 01873 890359
courtfarm@llanthony.co.uk
www.llanthonybunkbarn.co.uk
Court Farm, Llanthony, Abergavenny, Monmouthshire, NP7 7NN

THE STAR
BUNKHOUSE

An ideal base for exploring the beautiful Brecon Beacons National Park. The bunkhouse is situated in the village of Bwlch alongside the Beacons Way long distance footpath. Expect a warm & comfortable stay in this dog friendly bunkhouse with spacious bedrooms, cosy lounge/dining areas, fully-equipped kitchen, outside BBQ area, hot showers, drying room and car park. Accommodation for up to 20 people in bunkbeds in 6 bedrooms. Private bedrooms or sole use available. Individuals, couples & groups welcome.

DETAILS

- **Open** - All year. All day
- **Beds** - 20: 1x4 (en-suite), 3x4, 2x2
- **Price/night** - Standard rate £20pp

CONTACT: Emma & Peter Harrison
Tel: 01874 730080 or 07341 906937
info@starbunkhouse.com
www.starbunkhouse.com
Brecon Road (A40), Bwlch, Brecon,
Powys, LD3 7RQ

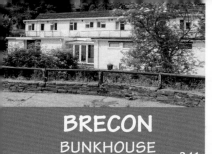

BRECON
BUNKHOUSE
241

Brecon Bunkhouse is a spacious, comfortable, bunkhouse in the Brecon Beacons. Great value self-catering accommodation with a big dining room and sitting room with wood-burner.

In the Black Mountains, with mountain walks from the door, an ideal base for horse riding, mountain biking and canoeing. There is a riding centre on the farm and the bunkhouse has a drying room and storage/cleaning facilities for bikes and canoes. Camping available.

DETAILS

- **Open** - All year. All day.
- **Beds** - 28: 1x10, 1x8, 1x6, 2x2,
- **Price/night** - £20pp, minimum of 4 people. £300 for exclusive use.

CONTACT: Paul and Emily Turner
Tel: 01874 711500
breconbunkhouse@gmail.com
www.brecon-bunkhouse.co.uk
Brecon Bunkhouse, Cwmfforest Farm,
Pengenfford, Talgarth, Brecon, LD3 0EU

THE DRAGONS
BACK

The Dragons Back (formerly The Castle Inn) is a pub with B&B, camping & 3 bunkrooms in the Brecon Beacons National Park. The bunkrooms are fully carpeted and centrally heated with en suite wet rooms, self-catering, drying facilities and secure storage. Stag/hens welcome. Dogs £5 pn in the bunkhouse. Meals in the pub. Glamping is available in our Shepherds Hut and the Tardis!

DETAILS

■ **Open** - All year. Arrive after 2pm, depart before 11 am.

■ **Beds** - 42: Bunkhouse 28: 1x6, 1x10, 1x12. B&B: 10: 4 rooms. Glamping: 2x2

■ **Price/night** - £17pp, £24pp with b/fast. Min of 5 people required for 6 bunk room, 7 for 10 b/room or 9 for 12 b/room. Sole use £425 or £625 with breakfast.

CONTACT: Jill Deakin
Tel: 01874 711353
info@thedragonsback.co.uk
www.thedragonsback.co.uk
Pengenffordd, LD3 0EP

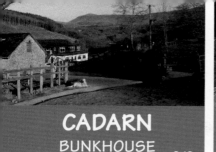

CADARN
BUNKHOUSE
243a

On a small hill farm in the Brecon Beacons National Park, Cadarn Bunkhouse is surrounded by views of the Black Mountains and the Wye Valley. With easy access to the mountains it is perfect for walking, mountain biking and horse riding whist the River Wye is great for canoeing. Self-catered bunkhouse, with the pub in Felindre half a mile away. Close to Hay on Wye and Brecon. Pony trekking available on-site, plus bike and canoe hire available locally.

DETAILS
■ **Open** - All year.
■ **Beds** - 57: Large Bunkhouse 47 in 7 rooms. Small Bunkhouse 9: 3x3
■ **Price/night** - From £16 pp.

CONTACT: Haydn Jones
Tel: 01497 847351
tregoydriding@btconnect.com
www.tregoydriding.co.uk
Tregoyd Mountain Riders, Lower Cwmcadarn Farm, Felindre, Three Cocks, Brecon, Powys, Wales LD3 0TB

WOODLANDS
BUNKHOUSE
243b

Woodlands Bunkhouse is a converted stable set in the 10 acre grounds of Woodlands Centre. It overlooks the River Wye and has wonderful views of the Black Mountains. The historic town of Hay on Wye is near by.

The Bunkhouse provides comfortable, modern accommodation for families and groups. There's a well equipped kitchen and dining room and 22 beds in 9 rooms. The bunkhouse can arrange courses in a variety of outdoor activities.

DETAILS
■ **Open** - All year. 24 hours.
■ **Beds** - 22 in rooms of 1 to 6 plus camping in the grounds.
■ **Price/night** - £16 pp + VAT. Reduction for children and large group bookings.

CONTACT: Annie Clipson
Tel: 01497 847272
annie.clipson@oxfordshireoutdoors.co.uk
www.woodlandsoec.org
Glasbury on Wye, Powys, HR3 5LP

CANTREF FARM
BUNKHOUSES
244a

RIVER CABIN
244b

Cantref Bunkhouses are in the foothills of the Brecon Beacons just outside the pretty market town of Brecon.

Ideal for groups of walkers, cyclists, climbers, canoeists, schools, clubs and families wanting to spend some quality time together. The 2 top quality bunkhouses provide self-catering or catered accommodation in private rooms with views overlooking the Brecon Beacons and the Black Mountains.

       GROUPS ONLY

River Cabin, let on a sole use basis for a min of 2 nights, is perfect for 2-4 people. Dog friendly with a secure garden, it overlooks a mill stream which feeds into the River Wye opposite. It has one cosy bunkroom (double bed & 2 bunks), a kitchen/lounge area, sunny dining porch, patio & private garden with picnic table, fire pit and BBQ. From Easter-Oct there's also a small campsite. Located on the Wye Valley Walk & NCN 8, it's a fantastic base for walkers & cyclists. Canoeing, pony trekking, gliding, bike hire, rope and climbing centre all close by.

DETAILS
- **Open** - All year
- **Beds** - 34: Large bunkhouse 24: 2x6, 2x4,1x2, 1x2 ensuite. Small bunkhouse 10: 2x4,1x2.
- **Price/night** - Please see website for prices and online booking.

CONTACT: Reception
Tel: 01874 665223
info@cantref.com
www.cantref.com
Cantref, Brecon Powys. LD3 8LR

DETAILS
- **Open** - All year, 24 hour access.
- **Beds** - 4: 1 x 4 (double & bunk beds)
- **Price/night** - From £30 per person per night, minimum stay 2 nights

CONTACT: Alistair / Nicky Legge
Tel: 07720 717124. 07740 290143
info@rivercabin.co.uk
www.rivercabin.co.uk
Erwood, Builth Wells, Powys, LD2 3TQ

DAN Y GYRN
BUNKHOUSE
245

Dan y Gyrn bunkhouse is the perfect base for walkers, cyclists, families or groups. Located in the heart of the Brecon Beacons it provides the ideal base to explore this National Park.

This comfortable, modern bunkhouse with amazing views is close to Pont ar Daf, the main access route to climb Pen Y Fan, so is great for walking groups. Ideal for families with a large garden for children to explore. Sleeping 15 in 2 rooms this well equipped bunkhouse is perfect for groups.

        GROUPS ONLY

DETAILS

- **Open** - All year. All day
- **Beds** - 15: 2x6, 1x3 campbeds
- **Price/night** - From £390 for two nights.

CONTACT: National Trust Holidays
Tel: 03443 351296
bunkhouses@nationaltrust.org.uk
www.nationaltrust.org.uk/holidays
Blaenglyn Farm, Libanus, Brecon,
Powys, LD3 8NF

CLYNGWYN
BUNKHOUSE

246

Clyngwyn 4* Bunkhouse sits in the Brecon Beacons, only minutes away from the waterfalls and caves of Ystradfellte and Sgwd Yr Eira.

Your ideal base for a wide range of outdoor activities. The bunkhouse sleeps up to 19, plus camping, three double B&B rooms and a romantic shepherd's hut in it's own private meadow.

DETAILS

■ **Open** - All year. All day.
■ **Beds** - Bunkhouse 19. B&B 6. Shepherd's Hut 2.
■ **Price/night** - Sun-Thurs: up to 19 people £285, up to 15 £230 or £18pp. Fri/Sat: up to 19 people £325, up to 15 £260. B&B £30pp. Shepherds hut £75 .

CONTACT: Julie Hurst
Tel: 01639 722930
enquiries@bunkhouse-south-wales.co.uk
www.bunkhouse-south-wales.co.uk
Clyngwyn Farm, Ystradfellte Rd,
Pontneddfechan, Powys, SA11 5US

CRAIG Y NOS
CASTLE

Craig Y Nos Castle sits in the Brecon Beacons. The Nurses Block can be booked on a daily or a room basis. It can also be booked sole use as group accommodation. Offering B&B or self-catering, the choice is yours. The castle provides hearty meals, cosy evenings by the wood burning stoves and a free history tour. Superior B&B rooms are available in the castle.

DETAILS

■ **Open** - All year
■ **Beds** - Nurses Block: 21: 10x2, 1x1. Castle: 67 rooms: (64 en suite)
■ **Price/night** - B&B £70 per twin bed room. Sole use of Bunkhouse: 1 night £350, 2 nights £500, 3 nights £600, 5 nights £700.

CONTACT: Reception
Tel: 01639 730725
info@craigynoscastle.com
www.craigynoscastle.com
Craig Y Nos Castle, Brecon Road,
Penycae, Powys, SA9 1GL

COED OWEN
BUNKHOUSE
248a

L&A
OUTDOOR CENTRE
248b

Set on a hill farm in the heart of the Brecon Beacons, 2 hours' walk from Pen Y Fan. This Bunkhouse provides well appointed self-catering accommodation; ideal for stag, hen and family parties.

Outdoor activities can be organised or there's direct access onto the mountains and waterfalls close by. Bike Park Wales, Merthyr Tydfil, Penderyn Whiskey and Brecon are all within easy reach. The pub, at the bottom of the drive, serves great food and fine ales.

L&A is set in a quiet wooded valley and offers accommodation for up to 280 people in self-catering cabins in the Swansea Bay area. There is a bar/café, commercial kitchen, activity hall, meeting rooms and 300 seat dining hall. Set in 80 acres of woodlands and pasture with open air swimming pool, BBQ and fire pits. L&A are happy to help you organise an event and have extensive links with activity providers in the area. Close to Afan Aergoed Mountain bike trails.

DETAILS

- **Open** - All year. All day.
- **Beds** - 26: 2x6, 1x10, 1 dbl, 1 twin.
- **Price/night** - From £22pp with bed linen. Min of two nights at weekends.

CONTACT: Molly or Netty Rees
Tel: 07508 544044 (8am-10pm)
info@breconbeaconsbunkhouse.co.uk
www.breconbeaconsbunkhouse.co.uk
Coed Owen Farm, Cwmtaff, Merthyr Tydfil , CF48 2HY

DETAILS

- **Open** - All day.
- **Beds** - Cabin: 117: 6/8 bed units. Bunkhouse: 175:10,16,24,30,40 bed.
- **Price/night** - Bunkhouses: from £12pp. Cabins: 6 bed £90-£150, 8 bed £100-£180. Enquire for group rates.

CONTACT: Matthew
Tel: 01639 885509
info@landaoutdoorcentre.co.uk
www.landaoutdoorcentre.co.uk
Goytre, West Glamorgan SA13 2YP

THE CHAPEL
HOUSE

Opened in summer 2019, The Chapel House is Swansea's only boutique hostel. Catering for travellers from around the world, it is nestled between the Castle and the Lighthouse, in the heart of the Mumbles.

Just 5 minutes away from Swansea centre and The Wales Coast Path. Within walking distance of great surf, walking and climbing. The perfect base for those seeking adventure on the Gower!

DETAILS

- **Open** - All year: Reception 3am-8pm. (Self check in optional)
- **Beds** - 20: 1x8, 2x4, 2x2
- **Price/night** - £15.99 pp. Private room for 2 £49.99. Group room for 3 £55.99. Exclusive hire £350.

CONTACT: Adam Gilbert
Tel: 01792 362 129 / 07717793890
Hello@thechapel.house
www.thechapel.house
18 Chapel Street, Mumbles, SA3 4NH

EASTERN SLADE
BARN

Eastern Slade Barn is a luxury farmhouse conversion on a working farm on the Gower Peninsula. The Gower has glorious beaches, castles & a network of traffic free lanes, ideal for mountain bikes. The Coastal Path passes through the farm. Port Eynon seaside village is a 30 min walk, while Oxwich Bay with its castle, beach & hotel serving tasty meals is just a 20 min walk. Camping is also available and weddings/birthdays can be accommodated.

DETAILS

- **Open** - All year. 24 hours.
- **Beds** - 15: 1x5, 2x2/3 (double with bunk above), 1x2, 2 in lounge
- **Price/night** - £15pp, £180 sole use. High season £20pp, £240 sole use.

CONTACT: Kate
Tel: 07970 969814
tynrheol@hotmail.com
www.easternsladebarngower.co.uk
Eastern Slade Farm, Oxwich, Gower, Swansea, SA3 1NA

RHOSSILI
BUNKHOUSE

251

Rhossili 4* Bunkhouse is situated at the end of the Gower Peninsula, in an Area of Outstanding Natural Beauty. It is within easy walking distance of three glorious beaches, (including Rhossili Bay voted the best beach in Europe and in the top ten in the World 2017). Ideal for families and groups and perfectly located for a wide range of outdoor activities including walking, surfing, cycling & climbing.

DETAILS

■ **Open** - All year except January. Check in 4-9pm; check out by 10:30am.
■ **Beds** - 18: 1x4, 2x3, 4x2. 4 sofa-beds in lounge (sole use).
■ **Price/night** - Shared (small groups) £16-£20. Full (group of 18) £340. Sole (group of 22) £390.

CONTACT: Josephine Higgins
Tel: 01792 391509
bookings@rhossili.org
www.rhossilibunkhouse.com
Rhossili Bunkhouse, Rhossili,
Swansea, SA3 1PL

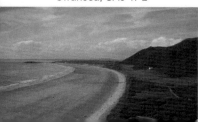

HARDINGSDOWN
BUNKHOUSE
252a

UPPER NEESTON
LODGES
252b

Hardingsdown Bunkhouse and The Chaffhouse both provide accommodation for families or groups. Comfortable and well appointed they are perfect for exploring Gower and all it has to offer. The properties can be hired individually or together, rates vary with numbers.

Environmentally sensitive barn conversions close to the Milford Haven Waterway in the Pembrokeshire Coast National Park. Ideal for divers, climbers, walkers or family get-togethers. The four independent 5* lodges have fully fitted kitchens and have access to garden/ patio, laundry/drying room, secure storage and ample parking.

DETAILS

- **Open** - All year. 24 hours.
- **Beds** - Bunkhouse 14: 1x5, 1x3, 3x2. Chaffhouse: 12: 1x4 4x2.
- **Price/night** - Hardingsdown Bunkhouse: (14 people max) £220 pn. The Chaffhouse: (12 people max) £220 pn. Midweek. £200 pn. Enquire for rates for both units together. Weekly rates available. INDIVIDUALS mid week only, £20 pppn (same for both properties).

DETAILS

- **Open** - All year. Check in from 4pm. Check out before 10.30am.
- **Beds** - 24: Cowshed 10: 1x6,1x4. Barn 8: 1x6,1x2, Granary 1x3. Dairy 1x3
- **Price/night** - From £17.50 (inc linen). Min 2 nights at w/ends (3 nights b/h). Sole use: min 6 Barn, 8 Cowshed. Smaller groups/individuals by agreement.

CONTACT: Allison Tyrrell
Tel: 01792 386222
bunkhousegower@btconnect.com
www.bunkhousegower.co.uk
Lower Hardingsdown Farm, Llangennith, Gower, Swansea, SA3 1HT

CONTACT: Sean or Mandy Tilling
Tel: 01646 690750
mail@upperneeston.co.uk
www.upperneeston.co.uk
Upper Neeston Farm, Dale Road, Herbrandston, Milford Haven, SA73 3RY

PANTYRATHRO

INTERNATIONAL HOSTEL

253

Llansteffan is a beautiful village at the tip of the Towi River & Carmarthen Bay. The sandy beaches below the castle offer sun bathing and relaxation.

The virtually traffic free country lanes are ideal for cycling. The Wales Coastal Path is on the doorstep and the city of Carmarthen is close by. The hostel provides dorm accommodation, private rooms, family rooms and en suite rooms.

DETAILS

- **Open** - February to January. 24 hours.
- **Beds** - 46: 1x10, 1x9, 1x6, 4x4, 1x3, 1x2
- **Price/night** - £17pp dorm. Group discounts. Different prices for different private rooms.

CONTACT: Ken Knuckles
Tel: 01267 241014
kenknuckles@hotmail.com
www.backpackershostelwales.com
Pantyrathro International Hostel,
Llansteffan, Carmarthen, SA33 5AJ

LAWRENNY

MILLENNIUM HOSTEL

Once a Victorian village school, the Lawrenny Hostel is superbly placed for exploring South Pembrokeshire. Warm, clean and comfortable, with modern facilities, the accommodation is ideal for individuals or groups, training courses or events. The adjoining village hall is also available to rent and there is a community shop, pub and an award-winning tearoom nearby.

DETAILS

■ **Open** - All year. All day. Arrange check in with warden.
■ **Beds** - 22: 2 x 4 (bunks), 2 x 4 (dbl + bunks), 1 x 6 (dbl/sgl + bunks)
■ **Price/night** - Adults £18, children (4-17) £12. Dbl rooms £40 (couple), £55 (with children). Sole use £300 per night

CONTACT: Laura Lort-Phillips
Tel: 01646 651270
hostel@lawrennyvillage.co.uk
www.lawrennyhostel.com
Lawrenny Millennium Hostel, Lawrenny, Pembrokeshire, SA68 0PW

STACKPOLE
CENTRE

The 150-bed, platinum eco-award-winning. Stackpole Centre is the perfect venue for large families/groups, special interest breaks and outdoor activities. It comprises four large houses, three cottages and a manor house. Close to wild woodlands and stunning beaches.

GROUPS ONLY

DETAILS

■ **Open** - All year. All day. Reception 9-5.
■ **Beds** - Kingfisher: 10 b/rooms (44 guests). Kestrel: 13 b/rooms (38 guests). Swan: 13 bedrooms (24 guests). Shearwater: 7 bedrooms (17 guests). Manor: 3 b/rooms (9 guests). 3 cottages: 9 b/rooms (18 guests).
■ **Price/night** - Whole site £2500, Kingfisher £695, Kestrel £425, Swan £595. Shearwater £325,

CONTACT: Stackpole Reception
Tel: 01646 623 110
stackpole.bookings@nationaltrust.org.uk
www.nationaltrust.org.uk/holidays
The Old Home Farm Yard, Stackpole, nr
Pembroke, Pembrokeshire, SA71 5DQ

WARREN FARM
GLAMPING

256

Beautiful big bell tents & a cosy bunkhouse, right on the Pembrokeshire Coast Path. Between Barafundle/ Broadhaven South & Freshwater West, and the closest you can stay to the Green Bridge of Wales. Perfect for family holidays or a quick surfing or climbing trip with friends. Simple, comfortable accommodation and private pitches with kitchens, loos & wetrooms for the bell tents. Don't delay, come glamping!

DETAILS

■ **Open** - All year. Check in 5-6pm, flexible by arrangement.
■ **Beds** - Bunkhouse: 12. Bell Tents: 6x8. Camping. Plus an expanding range of pods for couples & individuals.
■ **Price/night** - Check website for latest accommodation & prices. From £12pp.

CONTACT: Danielle, Jane or Hannah
stay@warrenfarm.wales
www.warrenfarm.wales
Warren Farm, Warren, near
Castlemartin, SA71 5HS

HAMILTON
BACKPACKERS

Hamilton Lodge - just one minute's walk from the centre of Fishguard and very close to the Pembrokeshire Coastal Path. Comfortable and friendly, sleeping nine in total with an en suite double and two dorms. Fully equipped kitchen, dining area and lounge. Charming, private garden and covered patio with seating. Free light breakfast included. Groups of up to 18 are welcome in collaboration with James John Hamilton House hostel next door.

DETAILS

■ **Open** - All year.
■ **Beds** - 9 (+10): 1 x 4, 1 x 3 and 1 x 2. (Plus 10 next door)
■ **Price/night** - From £20 to £21 pp in dorms, from £24.50 pp in double en suite.

CONTACT: Quentin Maclaurin
Tel: 01348 874797 or 07505 562939
hamiltonbackpackers@hotmail.com
www.hamiltonbackpackers.co.uk
23 Hamilton Street, Fishguard,
Pembrokeshire SA65 9HL

JAMES JOHN
HAMILTON HOUSE

258a

OLD SCHOOL
HOSTEL

258b

James John Hamilton House is a new conversion of the first free school in Fishguard, built in 1850 by James John Hamilton. The house provides comfortable, characterful self-catering accommodation for 12 people in five private rooms. Across the garden is Hamilton House Backpackers with an extra 9 beds. It's close to the centre of Fishguard with pubs & cafes. The Pembrokeshire Coastal Path passes through the town and communities of grey seals and dolphins are regularly seen in the local harbours.

Escape to this wonderful rugged corner of the Pembrokeshire Coast National Park. Old School Hostel is in Trefin, a pretty village which has a pub and a café, just a quarter of a mile from the world famous coast path. Circular walks from the door take you to stunning wild beaches & harbours. The cathedral city of St. Davids and the popular Whitesands Bay are 20 minutes by car.

DETAILS

■ **Open** - All year, but we strongly advise you check availability first.
■ **Beds** - 22: 1x6, 3x2, 2x2/3 (bunk with dbl lower bed), 1x4 (1 dbl + 1 bunk). Single occupancy available.
■ **Price/night** - From £25. Kids £15. Single occ from £35. Sole use from £330.

DETAILS

■ **Open** - All year.
■ **Beds** - 10 (+9): 1 x twin, 2 x dbl, 1 x 4 (dbl & bunk) plus 9 beds next door.
■ **Price/night** - From £20-£28 pp.

CONTACT: Steve Roberts
Tel: 01348 874288
stephenism@hotmail.com
www.jamesjohnhamilton.co.uk
19a Hamilton St, Fishguard SA65 9HL

CONTACT: Paul
Tel: 0784 562 5005
paul.moger@gmail.com
oldschoolhostel.com
Ffordd-yr-Afon, Trefin, Haverfordwest, Pembrokeshire, SA62 5AU

PRESELI VENTURE
ECO LODGE

259

Situated just a short walk to a stunning beach, this 5* Eco Lodge offers catered accommodation & a range of outdoor activities to individuals, families & groups of all sizes. Popular with schools, clubs & hen/stag groups it boasts great communal areas including a bar, outside picnic area, fire pit & games field. Just 1 mile from the Wales Coast Path & right on the Sustrans Celtic Trail.

DETAILS

- **Open** - All year (except Xmas)
- **Beds** - 40: 1x9, 1x6, 3x4, 1x3, 2x2, doubles x 3 + glamping/campsite
- **Price/night** - £45pp (incl breakfast), £69 (incl 3 meals). Under 17 £35pp (incl b/fast), £55 (3 meals)

CONTACT: Sophie or Ruth
Tel: 01348 837709
info@preseliventure.co.uk
www.preseliventure.co.uk/eco-lodge
Preseli Venture, Parc-y-nole Fach,
Mathry, Haverfordwest, Pembrokeshire,
SA62 5HN

CAERHAFOD
LODGE
260

Situated between the famous cathedral city of St Davids and the Irish ferry port of Fishguard, the 4* Lodge overlooks the spectacular Pembrokeshire coastline. Within walking distance of the Sloop Inn at Porthgain and the internationally renowned Coastal Path. An ideal stopover for cyclists with The Celtic Trail cycle route passing the bottom of the drive. The lodge sleeps 23 in 5 separate rooms, all en suite with great showers. Dogs welcome by arrangement.

DETAILS
- **Open** - All year. Check in from 4pm, check out 10.30 am. All day access.
- **Beds** - 23: 3x4, 1x5, 1x6.
- **Price/night** - Adult £22. Under 16s £16. Exclusive use group rates available.

CONTACT: Carolyn Rees
Tel: 01348 837859
Caerhafod@aol.com
www.caerhafod.co.uk
Llanrhian, St Davids, Haverfordwest, Pembrokeshire, SA62 5BD

THE LONG BARN

Penrhiw is an organic farm with views over the Teifi Valley. The stunning Ceredigion Coast and the Cambrian Mountains are an easy drive away and the busy small town of Llandysul (1.5 miles) has all essential supplies. The farm's location is ideal for exploring, studying or simply admiring the Welsh countryside. Local activities include fishing, swimming, climbing, abseiling, canoeing, farm walks and cycling.

DETAILS

- **Open** - All year. All day.
- **Beds** - 43: Long Barn 31: 1x15, 1x14, 1x2. Cowshed: 6:1x6. Annex 3: 1x3 (dbl+sgl). Cwtsh 3: 1x3 (dbl+sofa bed)
- **Price/night** - £15pp. Discount for groups and mid week bookings.

CONTACT: Tom or Eva
Tel: 01559 363200, Mob 07733 026874
cowcher@thelongbarn.co.uk
www.thelongbarn.co.uk
Penrhiw, Capel Dewi, Llandysul,
Ceredigion, SA44 4PG

GILFACH WEN
BARN

262

A homely, high quality, bunkhouse for individuals, extended families or groups on a working farm. The large social area is ideal for reunions or celebrations. There are 7 family bedrooms including one downstairs for disabled. Perfect for exploring Carmarthenshire, Pembrokeshire, Brecon Beacons, Cambrian Mountains and the Gower. Walker, cyclist, dog & equestrian friendly. Village pub close by.

DETAILS

- **Open** - All year. All day.
- **Beds** - 32: 3x6,1x5,1x4,1x3,1x2. Total 10 double & 12 singles in 7 bedrooms.
- **Price/night** - From £17.50pp. Groups only at weekends and school hols. Last min weekends £20pp if not booked up.

CONTACT: Jillie
Tel: 07780 476737
info@gilfachwenbarn.co.uk
www.gilfachwenbarn.co.uk
Gilfach Wen, Brechfa,
Carmarthenshire, SA32 7QL

DINEFWR
BUNKHOUSE
263

On a National Trust estate one mile from Llandeilo, Dinefwr Bunkhouse sits in the heart of an 18th century park enclosing a medieval deer park, next to the historic Newton House. Quite the perfect holiday location for groups or families who enjoy walking or other outdoor activities.

This beautifully presented, characterful bunkhouse sleeps up to 16 in a 7 bed dorm and 2, 3 & 4 bedded rooms. It has a well equipped kitchen for self-catering.

DETAILS
- **Open** - All year. All day
- **Beds** - 16: 1x7, 1x4, 1x2, 1x2 + double
- **Price/night** - For groups of 8 or less from £160 per night. Extra £20 per person per night for parties with over 8 people.

CONTACT: National Trust Holidays
Tel: 03443 351296
bunkhouses@nationaltrust.org.uk
www.nationaltrust.org.uk/holidays
Dinefwr Park, Llandeilo,
Carmarthenshire, SA19 6RT

TYNCORNEL
HOSTEL
264

Tyncornel is a former farmhouse set in stunning Cambrian Mountain scenery at the head of the beautiful Doethie Valley. It is one of the most remote hostels in Wales, favoured by walkers, cyclists, and bird watchers. It is on the Cambrian Way long distance footpath. The hostel has 16 places. There is a cosy common room with wood-burning stove, two dormitories with built-in bunk beds and a self-catering kitchen.

DETAILS
- **Open** - All year. Reception 5pm -11pm, 7am -10am.
- **Beds** - 16: 2x8.
- **Price/night** - £14 per adult, £7 (under 18s). Whole hostel bookings £200 and private rooms available. Campers £8.

CONTACT: Janet or Richard
Tel: 01980 629259
Tyncornel.bookings@btinternet.com
www.elenydd-hostels.co.uk
Llanddewi Brefi, Tregaron,
Ceredigion, SY25 6PH

DOLGOCH
HOSTEL

Experience the peace of the remote Tywi valley in an era before electricity at this 17th century farmhouse. Dolgoch is a traditional simple hostel owned by the Elenydd Wilderness Trust. It has hot showers, log burner, self-catering kitchen, dormitories & private rooms. The Lôn Las Cymru and the Cambrian Way pass nearby and there are many mountain tracks to explore. Ideal for bird-watchers and lovers of the solitude of the scenic Cambrian Mountains.

DETAILS
- **Open** - All year. 24 hours. Reception 5pm -11pm, 8am -10am.
- **Beds** - 20: 3 rooms inc private rooms.
- **Price/night** - £14 per adult, £7 (under 18). Campers £8 .

CONTACT: Gillian Keen
Tel: 01440 730226
gill.keen@dolgoch.org
www.elenydd-hostels.co.uk
Dolgoch, Tregaron,
Ceredigion, SY25 6NR

NATURESBASE
HOLIDAYS
266a

Nestled between the Cambrian Mountains and Cardigan Bay, Naturesbase is 9 acres of flower rich meadows and woodland, 10 minutes drive from the Welsh coast. With a mixture of wooden lodges, camping, barn and a shepherds hut, Naturesbase is ideal for families, couples and groups wanting to enjoy the open countryside and all that nature has to offer.

DETAILS
■ **Open** - All year, Camping summer only.
■ **Beds** - Group accom. 36:4x2,4x4, 2x6. Summer Lodges:16:4x4, 6:1x6, 6:1x6. Shepherds hut: 2+2 kids. 10 pitches.
■ **Price/night** - Groups £25pp min 2 night, min 12 people. Camping from £25 for 2 people.

CONTACT: Gyles or Alison
Tel: 01570 471795 or 07773 817058
gyles@naturesbase.co.uk
naturesbase.co.uk
Tyngwndwn Farm, Cilcennin, Lampeter, Ceredigion, SA48 8RJ

STONECROFT
LODGE
266b

Stonecroft Lodge is in Llanwrtyd Wells, the smallest town in Britain. Surrounded by the green fields and mountains of mid Wales, Llanwrtyd is in renowned red kite country and is a great base for mountain biking, walking & pony trekking.

The hostel has private rooms with made-up beds, a fully equipped kitchen, lounge with TV, free laundry and drying, central heating, a large riverside garden and ample parking. The hostel adjoins the Stonecroft Inn for great beer & food.

DETAILS
■ **Open** - All year. All day. Call on arrival.
■ **Beds** - 27: 1x1, 3x4, 1x6, 4x(dbl+sgl)
■ **Price/night** - £16. Discounts for 3+ nights. Phone for sole use rates.

CONTACT: Jane Brown
Tel: 01591 610332
party@stonecroft.co.uk
www.stonecroft.co.uk
Dolecoed Road, Llanwrtyd Wells, Powys, LD5 4RA

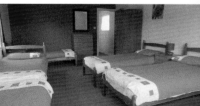

BEILI NEUADD
BUNKHOUSE

A converted 18th century stone barn in stunning countryside just 2 miles from the small market town of Rhayader - the gateway to the Elan Valley and Cambrian Mountains. On three National Cycle routes and the Trans Cambrian Route. Beili Neuadd offers lovely gardens, ponds and stunning scenery. The centrally heated barn sleeps 16 in 3 en suite rooms and includes a fully equipped kitchen/dining room and drying room. There is also camping space in the paddock.

DETAILS

■ **Open** - All year. All day.
■ **Beds** - 16: 2x6,1x4. B&B: 3 x double.
■ **Price/night** - £20 per person for 1 night, £19 per person 2 nights or more, sole occupancy £275.

CONTACT: Ruth Ward
Tel: 01597 810211
info@beilineuadd.co.uk
www.beilineuadd.co.uk
Beili Neuadd, Rhayader, LD6 5NS

MID WALES
BUNKHOUSE

Mid Wales Bunkhouse has a superb unspoilt rural location, close to the Elan Valley, for any activity or occasion with a stunning natural garden. Explore or swim in the river. There's walking and biking from the door, even accommodation for your horse. Fully equipped for self catering or meals provided. Authentic tipi and camping. Available for groups of up to 26 or individuals.

DETAILS

- **Open** - All year. 24 hours. Arrive after 4pm (advise if after 7pm), leave by 11am.
- **Beds** - 20
- **Price/night** - £17pp, £90 for private 6-bed room. Sole use of dormitory area (sleeps 14) £195 per night. Sole use of bunkhouse (20 people) £260 per night.

CONTACT: John
Tel: 01597 870081 or 07507 343262
enquiries@bunkhousemidwales.co.uk
www.bunkhousemidwales.co.uk
Woodhouse Farm, St Harmon,
Rhayader, LD6 5LY

HAFREN FOREST
BUNKHOUSE
269a

PLASNEWYDD
BUNKHOUSE
269b

This former weather station has been converted into a comfortable bunkhouse on the edge of the Hafren Forest. It is close to Plumlimon, in a quiet rural location between Llanidloes & Machynlleth in the Cambrian Mountains. A great base for Glyndwrs Way, The Sustrans 8, Trans Cambrian Way, kayaking, mountain biking, fly fishing, family groups & parties. Fully central heated with a large dining room, well equipped kitchen & comfortable lounge. Private bedrooms. Breakfast & evening meal available if pre booked.

Set in the beautiful Mid Wales countryside on the Glyndwrs Way, the 4* bunkhouse is an ideal location for exploring or unwinding. Built to the highest standards it provides high quality accommodation for groups or individuals. It can also be booked for conferences and seminars. Attractions close by include sailing, golf course, outdoor pursuit centre, shooting range, motorbike school and the picturesque market town of Llanidloes (1/2 mile) with many places to eat and drink.

DETAILS
- **Open** - All year.
- **Beds** - 19: 1x5, 1x6, 2x4
- **Price/night** - £20 per person.

DETAILS
- **Open** - All year. 24 hours. Arrival and departure times by arrangement.
- **Beds** - 27 in 2 dorms + 1 family room.
- **Price/night** - £20pp + £3 for bedding if required. Sole use £403.

CONTACT: Darren and Sarah
Tel: 07871 740514
mrsh66@btinternet.com
www.hafrenforestbunkhouse.com
Staylittle, nr Llanidloes, Powys,
SY19 7DB

CONTACT: Susan
Tel: 01686 412431 or 07975 913049
susanvaughan67@aol.co.uk
www.plasnewyddbunkhouse.co.uk
Gorn Rd, Llanidloes, Powys, SY18 6LA

BWTHYN
BACH

270

Bwthyn Bach, in the village of Trefeglwys in rural Mid Wales is run by a small trust. Sleeping 17 across 5 rooms, the facilities are simple & add to the quaint & quirky feel of this 300 year old Grade II building.
There's a small kitchen/diner with hot water, kettle, electric cooker, microwave & all the basic crockery/cutlery you will need. A wood burning Rayburn keeps it warm, while a separate dining room has space for large groups. BYO bedding.

       GROUPS ONLY

DETAILS

- **Open** - All year.
- **Beds** - 17: 1x6/7, 1x3/4, 1x2/3, 1xdbl, 1xsgl + camping
- **Price/night** - £20pp. Children & Concessions £12pp. Capped at a max of £100 per night. Sole use only.

CONTACT: Amy
Tel: 07975 994164
hello@bwthynbach.com
www.bwthynbach.com
Bwthyn Bach, Trefeglwys, Caersws, Powys. SY17 5QE

ABERYSTWYTH
UNI BUNKHOUSE
271

Aberystwyth University Bunkhouse is on the Wales Coast Path, close to beaches, dramatic walking and white knuckle mountain biking. Aberystwyth has all the attractions of a Victorian seaside town with the added adventure of an ancient castle and thriving nightlife. Accommodation is in single rooms with shared self-catering kitchens and bathrooms. Meals available. Ideal for education trips, conference, or those looking for a base for a family seaside holiday or outdoor group trip.

DETAILS
- **Open** - All year. Reception 9am-5pm.
- **Beds** - 90 : Individual bedrooms
- **Price/night** - £30 (2+nights) or £36. Reduced rates for educational groups.

CONTACT: Conference Office
Tel: 01970 621960
constaff@aber.ac.uk
www.aber.ac.uk/en/visitors/bunkhouse
Penbryn Reception, Aberystwyth
University, Penbryn, Penglais, SY23 3BY

PLAS DOLAU

COUNTRY HOUSE HOSTEL

272

Plas Dolau is set in 25 acres just 3 miles from Aberystwyth. Ideal for exploring West Wales, walking, cycling, riding, fishing and golf. The warm country mansion has mainly dormitory style accommodation for up to 45 people.

An adjoining Swedish style farmhouse can take another 15. Plas Dolau includes meeting rooms, dining rooms, a games room & outdoor areas. Ideally suited for youth groups, field courses, retreats, house parties or individuals.

DETAILS

- **Open** - All year. 24 hours.
- **Beds** - 45:+cots. Plus 16 in farmhouse.
- **Price/night** - From £22 (inc breakfast) to £40 (private, en suite, full breakfast). From £675 for the whole mansion.

CONTACT: Pat Twigg
Tel: 01970 617834
pat@plasdolau.co.uk
www.plasdolau.co.uk
Lovesgrove, Aberystwyth, SY23 3HP

BORTH
YOUTH HOSTEL
273a

With 4 miles of stunning beach just 20 metres from the front door, Borth Youth Hostel is perfect for a beach holiday. This Edwardian house has 9 bedrooms with sea views and is a great base for visits to the Centre for Alternative Technology, Aberystwyth or the beautiful Dyfi Biosphere. Snowdonia National Park is just a short drive away making Borth perfect for both mountain biking & surfing. With two classrooms, Borth YHA is ideal for school trips too. There's free WiFi, a games & TV room, bike storage & drying room. Breakfast, packed lunch & a licensed bar are available.

DETAILS

■ **Open** - All year. Check in 5 - 10.30pm. Check out 8am - 10am
■ **Beds** - 60
■ **Price/night** - From £18 pp

CONTACT: John Taylor
Tel: 01970 871498
john@borthyouthhostel.co.uk
Borth, Ceredigion, Wales, SY24 5JS

TOAD HALL
273b

Toad Hall sits beside the River Dovey, close to Snowdonia National Park in the market town of Machynlleth. NCN Cycle Route 8 & Glyndwrs Way pass near by. The hostel consists of a three bed-roomed self contained unit above the owner's family home. The small flat garden is ideal for camping and there's a small workshop for bike repair/storage.

DETAILS

■ **Open** - Not always open, please phone to find out and always pre-book. Please vacate rooms from 12 - 1 pm for cleaning. No arrivals after 11pm please.
■ **Beds** - 9: 1x4(dbl+twin), 1x3(dbl+sgl), 1x2(twin)
■ **Price/night** - £18 pp. Reductions (e.g. for groups) negotiable

CONTACT: Will
Tel: 01654 700597 or 07866 362507 or text 07962 995168
willcoyn@hotmail.com
Railway Terrace, Doll St, Machynlleth, Powys, SY20 8BH

CORRIS
HOSTEL
274

Perfect for group & family celebrations, Corris hostel is a haven from the stresses of the outside world with its caring staff & cosy wood fires. Enjoy the gardens with BBQ & campfire areas.

Situated in Snowdonia National Park close to Cadair Idris, the Centre for Alternative Technology and just 3 miles from the new Dyfi Bike Park, a mecca for trail bikers. A real paradise for outdoor enthusiasts. CAMRA pub close by.

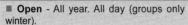

DETAILS
- **Open** - All year. All day (groups only winter).
- **Beds** - 43: 1x18, 1x10, 1x6, 1x4, 1x double+2, 1x double+1,
- **Price/night** - Adult from £20, child £14. Breakfast £4.50. Private rooms extra.

CONTACT: Faye, Michael or Debbie
Tel: 01654 761686
mail@corrishostel.co.uk
Old School, Corris, Machynlleth, Powys, SY20 9TQ

TORRENT WALK
BUNKHOUSE
275a

HYB BUNKHOUSE
DOLGELLAU
275b

Torrent Walk Bunkhouse is ideal for exploring Snowdonia. Newly refurbished, it sleeps 36 in 6 rooms. Centrally heated, there's a well equipped kitchen/diner & a power shower block by the door.

There are lots of walks on the doorstep & for mountain bikers Coed-y-Brenin & Mawddach are close by as is the seaside town of Barmouth.

Apartments, B&B & camping on site. BYO bedding or hire. No under 16s.

HyB Bunkhouse is in Dolgellau (Lon Las, Sustrans 82), Mid Wales, at the foot of Cader Idris. Centrally located above Medi Gifts, with free parking at rear for up to four cars, there are shops, pubs and restaurants on the doorstep. HyB backs onto the Mawddach trail near the river Wnion and it is 10 minutes' drive to Coed y Brenin mountain biking centre. This quirky listed building has original features such as oak floors, beams and paneling and offers a good night's sleep. No stag weekends or parties in this quiet bunkhouse.

DETAILS
■ **Open** - All year. Check in 1pm/check out 11am.
■ **Beds** - 36: 6x6
■ **Price/night** - £17pp (£15 for 2 nights+)

CONTACT: Gail or Evelina
Tel: 01341 422 269
dolgunuchaf@aol.com
guesthousessnowdonia.com
Dolgun Uchaf, Nr Dolgellau, Snowdonia, Gwynedd LL40 2AB

DETAILS
■ **Open** - All year, not New Year & Xmas.
■ **Beds** - 16: 4 x 4 rooms
■ **Price/night** - £20 per person. Limited bedding sets available for £5.

CONTACT: Nia
Tel: 01341 421755
post@medi-gifts.com
2-3 Heol y Bont (Bridge St), Dolgellau, Gwynedd, LL40 1AU

PLAS ISA

276a

FFRIDD
BUNKHOUSE

276b

In the centre of Dolgellau, Plas Isa welcomes independent travellers to this historic Welsh town. The communal lounge and dining room are great for socialising with your group or other guests. It is the perfect base for active holidays in Snowdonia for walkers (Cader Idris, Snowdonia Way), mountain bikers (Coed y Brenin) and cyclists (Mawddach Trail, Lon Las Cymru).

Remote & peaceful, surrounded by the rugged splendour of Snowdonia, Ffridd Bunkhouse offers budget accommodation. Harlech with its beach, pubs, cafes & castle is just 2.5 miles away. This basic accommodation is in 2 units, one sleeps 12 & the other 4/5. Both have kitchen/dining areas & some heating. Each has a separate outside WC, but the shower is shared. Walkers, climbers & mountain bikers alike return annually to this hidden gem of a bunkhouse. BYO bedding.

DETAILS

- **Open** - All year. Check in after 3pm, check out before 10am.
- **Beds** - 19: 2x3, 2x4, 1x5
- **Price/night** - From £25pp (family room 3+). Dbl/twin: £30pp. Single: £40pp. U10 £15pp (at least 1 adult in room). Sole occupancy £400. Prices include continental style breakfast (excl sole occ).

DETAILS

- **Open** - All year.
- **Beds** - 18: 1x12, 1x5/6 (4 bunks/1 dbl)
- **Price/night** - £6pp. Min 4 people/£24. Discounts for large groups.

CONTACT: Ian and Hanneke
Tel: 01341 423178 or 07984 737066
info@plasisaguesthouse.co.uk
www.plasisaguesthouse.co.uk
Lion Street, Dolgellau, LL40 1DG

CONTACT: Wil
Tel: 01766 780329 or (07787 146 907)
enquiries@ffridd.org
www.ffridd.org
Ffridd Llwyn Gwerfyl, Harlech,
Gwynedd, LL46 2TW

BUNKORAMA

Whether you're a lone cyclist or a group of walkers you will love discovering this cosy, clean and comfortable accommodation with breathtaking views of Cader Idris and Cardigan Bay.

Handy for Cycle Route 8, the Cambrian Way & Mawddach Trail and at only £15 per night Bunkorama is an ideal place to make a stopover or spend a few days exploring the mountains, rivers and beaches of the Cambrian Coast.

DETAILS

- **Open** - All year.
- **Beds** - 8: 2x4, plus sofa bed in lounge.
- **Price/night** - £17 pp (£18 pp winter) + £5 per stay if bedding needed and towel available £2 per stay

CONTACT: Graham
Tel: 01341 281134 or 07738 467196
thebunkorama@gmail.com
www.bunkorama.co.uk
Gwastad Agnes Off Panorama Road,
Barmouth, Gwynedd, LL42 1DX

BUNKHOUSE
AT THE WORKHOUSE 278

The well equipped, community run bunkhouse at Y Dolydd Llanfyllin Workhouse is handy for Welshpool & Shrewsbury and close to the Berwyn Mountains. With access to a wide range of adventurous activities including Lake Vyrnwy, Pistyll Rhaeadr waterfall (the tallest in the UK) and Revolution bike park. Venue hire for events welcomed, catering/bar available by arrangement. Visit the free History Centre to learn more about the building and the people who lived and worked in it.

   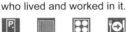

DETAILS

- **Open** - All year.
- **Beds** - 24: 1x4, 1x8, 1x12
- **Price/night** - £16 incl. linen, duvets & pillow. Group discounts may apply.

CONTACT: Liz Neal
Tel: 07757 233573
bunkhouse@the-workhouse.com
www.the-workhouse.org.uk
Y Dolydd, Workhouse,
Llanfyllin, SY22 5LD

BALA
BACKPACKERS
279a

BALA
BUNK HOUSE
279b

For outdoor adventures within the Snowdonia National Park, Bala Backpackers offers great value 'hostel-style' accommodation, including; 30+ comfy SINGLE BEDS in bedrooms of 3,4 or 5, 3 private TWIN ROOMS and 3 new EN SUITES. Located in a quiet, sunny, chapel square, in the bustling market town of Bala with its five-mile-long lake and white-water river for raft rides.

A converted 200 year old stone building, Bala Bunk House is full of character. Set back from the road in over an acre of grounds with private parking and views of the Berwyn Hills. Ideal for all types of groups, family parties & individuals. Close to many outdoor activity centres and all amenities. It is the perfect base for walkers & water sport enthusiasts with Bala Lake & the National White Water Centre on the doorstep.

DETAILS

- **Open** - All year by arrangement. 8.30-20.30. Front door locked 00.30 - 6.00am.
- **Beds** - Maximum: 45: 2x3, 3x4, 3x5 + 3 twin rooms + 3 en suites.
- **Price/night** - 1 night £21, 2 nights £39, 3 nights £49, weekly £89. Twin room: £49 or en suites from £59. Double holiday-let: £220/4 nights. Sheet-bag hire £3/week.

DETAILS

- **Open** - All year. No restrictions. Telephone 9am - 7pm
- **Beds** - 26: 1x2,1x4,1x6,1x8. 1x6 self-contained.
- **Price/night** - Single night from £18 pp, two+ nights from £16.50 pp.

CONTACT: Stella Shaw
Tel: 01678 521700
info@bala-backpackers.co.uk
www.Bala-Backpackers.co.uk
32 Tegid Street, Bala, LL23 7EL

CONTACT: Guy and Jane Williams
Tel: 01678 520738
thehappyunion@btinternet.com
www.balabunkhouse.co.uk
Tomen Y Castell, Llanfor, Bala,
Gwynedd, LL23 7HD

LLANGOLLEN
HOSTEL

280

Llangollen Hostel, in the Dee Valley is perfect for walking, cycling, canoeing & white water rafting. Families will love visiting the steam railway, horse drawn canal boats & Pontcysyllte Aqueduct - a World Heritage Site. The town has a great choice of restaurants/pubs. It is home to a fringe music & arts festival & the International Eisteddfod. Llandegla, Chester, Wrexham & Offa's Dyke Path are all nearby. A warm welcome awaits!

DETAILS

■ **Open** - All year. All day.
■ **Beds** - 31: 2x6, 1x4/5, 2x4, 1x3/4, 1x2/3, 1x2
■ **Price/night** - From £19pp dorm. £20pp for 3,4,5 or 6 bed room. £45 twin/double or £50 en suite. Family of 4 £60, £10 per extra child. Book direct for the best prices.

CONTACT: Arlo Dennis
Tel: 01978 861773
info@llangollenhostel.co.uk
www.llangollenhostel.co.uk
Berwyn Street, Llangollen, LL20 8NB

HENDRE ISAF
BASECAMP
281

This converted Grade II stone farm building is the perfect base for enjoying the Snowdonia National Park. Part of the 8,000 hectare Ysbyty Estate, it offers spacious, well appointed group accommodation.

Local attractions include the Tree Top Adventure Course at Betws-y-Coed, Zip World at Penrhyn Quarry, Bethesda, Zip World and Bounce Below at Llechwedd Slate Caverns, Blaenau Ffestiniog and the Plas y Brenin National Mountain Centre.

      GROUPS ONLY

DETAILS

- **Open** - All year. 24 hours.
- **Beds** - 18: 2 x dormitories + 1x1.
- **Price/night** - 2 nights from £380.

CONTACT: National Trust Holidays
Tel: 03443 351296
bunkhouses@nationaltrust.org.uk
www.nationaltrust.org.uk/holidays
National Trust Ysbyty Estate Office,
Dinas, Betws-y-Coed, Conwy, LL24 0HF

TYDDYN BYCHAN

282a

VAGABOND
BUNKHOUSE

282b

Tyddyn Bychan is an 18th century Welsh farm surrounded by fields. It is an excellent self-catering base for mountain biking, road cycling, canoeing, walking, climbing, fishing and numerous watersports including white water rafting. The main bunkhouse sleeps 18 in two en suite rooms. All bunks are handmade to a very high standard. The smaller bunkhouse sleeps 9 in two en suite rooms. All bedding is included. Delicious homemade food is available if booked in advance. There is a good parking area well away from the road.

The Vagabond Bunkhouse/Hostel is in the village of Betws-y-Coed, in the heart of Snowdonia National Park. This unique bunkhouse has been specifically designed for individuals, families or groups. Very well appointed, it has ready made up beds, free hot drinks, seriously hot showers, a well equipped kitchen & a bar. Catering is available & there is a Pizza restaurant on site (notice required). Outside there's a climbing wall, a power wash & heated dog kennels!

        GROUPS ONLY

DETAILS
- **Open** - All year. All day.
- **Beds** - 27: 1x10; 1x8; 1x6; 1x3
- **Price/night** - £18 pp including bedding

CONTACT: Lynda
Tel: 01490 420680 or 07523 995741
lynda@tyddynbychan.co.uk
www.tyddynbychan.co.uk
Cefn Brith, Cerrigydrudion, Conwy,
LL21 9TS

DETAILS
- **Open** - All year. Reception open 7.30-10am and 4.30-7.30pm.
- **Beds** - 36: 2x8, 2x6, 2x4
- **Price/night** - £22.00pp. B&B (obligatory at weekends) £27.00. Heated dog kennel £3.00 per night.

CONTACT: Neil Cawthra
Tel: 01690 710850 or 07816 076546
neilcawthra@mail.com
www.thevagabond.co.uk
Craiglan, Betws-y-Coed, LL24 0AW

WOODLANDS
CENTRE
283

This large Victorian property has been specially adapted to provide self-catering accommodation for groups of up to 33. The eight dormitories vary in size from one to ten beds, complete with duvets and linen. The Centre is centrally heated and has a common room, games room, large kitchen, drying room and hot showers. Located in Betws-y-Coed, Woodlands Centre is an ideal base for outdoor activities in Snowdonia.

DETAILS

- **Open** - All year. All day
- **Beds** - 33: 1x10,1x8,1x4,2x3,2x2,1x1
- **Price/night** - £18.15 pp. Sole Use: youth groups £216.44. Adult only groups £471.90. Further reductions for members and uniformed organisations-see website.

CONTACT: Lisa Pratt
Tel: 01690 710863
BookingOffice@WoodlandsCentre.com
www.woodlandscentre.com
Vicarage Road, Betws-y-Coed,
Conwy, LL24 0AD

LLEDR HOUSE

Lledr House nestles in Snowdonia National Park. Once YHA and now newly refurbished, guests delight in the luxury mattresses, modern bathrooms, well equipped kitchen and extended car park. Individuals, groups and families enjoy the clean, comfortable accommodation.

Betws-y-Coed, Llyn Elsi and Zip World high rope course close by.

DETAILS

■ **Open** - Open March to November incl. Check in from 5pm till 10.30pm.
■ **Beds** - 37: House 32: 1x9, 2x4,1x6, 2x2, 2x2(dbl), 2x1. Cabin 5: 1x5
■ **Price/night** - From £18.00pp. Single rooms £22.50. Sole Use: £575 (min 3 nights on BH). Cabin £120 (min 2 nights).

CONTACT: Brian or Melanie Quilter
Tel: 07915 397660
Lledrhouse@aol.com
lledrhouse.co.uk
Pont-y-Pant, Dolwyddelan,
North Wales, LL25 0DQ

ELENS CASTLE
HOTEL BUNKROOM
285a

OGWEN VALLEY
BUNKHOUSE
285b

Situated in the beautiful Lledr Valley between Betws-y-Coed and Blaenau Ffestiniog in Snowdonia National Park, Elens Castle Hotel Bunkroom offers budget accommodation within a cosy hotel setting. The 4 bed en suite bunkroom can be booked by the bed or the room. Self catering is not available but bunkroom guests are invited to socialise and eat in the hotel. BYO bedding & towels.

An ideal base for exploring Snowdonia .

In Snowdonia National Park, just over a mile from the small town of Bethesda, Ogwen Valley Bunkhouse provides spacious, eco friendly accommodation for individuals, couples, families and groups. The large open plan communal area has a well equipped kitchen, a large dining table and plenty of comfy chairs.

With a log burning stove, underfloor heating, comfortable beds and a drying room guests invariably return. It is on the Snowdonia Slate Trail and the Lon Las Cymru cycling route.

DETAILS

■ **Open** - 1st April - 1st Oct. Check in after 3 pm. Check out by 10.30 am.
■ **Beds** - 4: 1x4
■ **Price/night** - £10 pp (breakfast £7.50).

CONTACT: Helen & Adam Hardy
Tel: 01690 750207
stay@hotelinsnowdonia.co.uk
www.hotelinsnowdonia.co.uk
Dolwyddelan, Betws-y-Coed,
Snowdonia, North Wales LL25 0EJ

DETAILS

■ **Open** - All year. Check out 10.30
■ **Beds** - 16: 2x4, 1x6, 1x camp bed, 1x bed settee
■ **Price/night** - £17pp

CONTACT: Gwyn Morgan
Tel: 01248 601958 or 07775978405
bookings@ogwenvalleybunkhouse.co.uk
www.ogwenvalleybunkhouse.co.uk
Capel Saron, Tyn Y Maes, Bethesda,
Gwynedd LL57 3LX

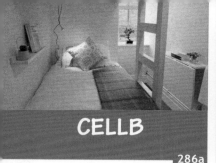

CELLB

286a

After a long day of adventures, why not rest your weary head in an Edwardian police house hostel?

Conveniently located in the centre of Blaenau Ffestiniog. There is a self-catering kitchen, a drying room and secure bike / climbing gear storage.

CellB is the perfect place to recover, recuperate, and soak up the vibrant landscape.

DETAILS
- **Open** - All year. All day
- **Beds** - 11: 1x6, 1x3, 1x2
- **Price/night** - From £20. Sole use from £396 for the weekend (Friday-Sunday) £1,386 for the week.

CONTACT: Reception
Tel: 01766 832001
hostelcellb@outlook.com
cellb.org
Park Square, Blaenau
Ffestiniog LL41 3AD

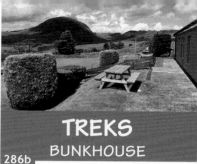

TREKS
BUNKHOUSE

286b

Treks 4* Bunkhouse is in the mountains on the edge of the village of Blaenau Ffestiniog. Ideal for enjoying the rugged beauty of Snowdonia, it's a former golf club recently converted to provide self-catering accommodation for individuals & groups. Numerous attractions nearby include, Llechwedd Slate Caverns, Bounce Below, Zip World Titan, Antur Stiniog, Ffestiniog Railway, Welsh Highland Railway, Go Below Adventures, Coed y Brenin Mountain Bike Centre, Portmeirion Italian Village, Bala White Water Rafting, Harlech Castle, Black Rock Sands. And many more!!

DETAILS
- **Open** - All year. Check in 15:00-20:00
- **Beds** - 16: 1x6, 1x4, 1x3, 1x2, 1x1
- **Price/night** - £22 per person

CONTACT: Dyfed
Tel: 07796 172318
treksbunkhouse@gmail.com
www.treksbunkhouse.co.uk
Y Cefn, Ffestiniog, Gwynedd, LL41 4PS

SNOWDON LODGE
GROUP HOSTEL

287

Stay in the birthplace of Lawrence of Arabia! Snowdon Lodge provides self-catering group accommodation. Located in the village of Tremadog, Snowdon Lodge is perfect for family reunions or groups wanting to explore Snowdonia and the Llyn Peninsula. It has 10 rooms (twins, doubles and small dormitories), an additional lecture room and a large car park leading to woodland walks.

       GROUPS ONLY

DETAILS

- **Open** - January - December. All day.
- **Beds** - 35: 2 x 6 (family), 1 x 5, 1 x 6, 3 x twin, 3 x double
- **Price/night** - Sole use £600 per night. Min of 2 nights, 3 on bank holidays. Discounts for longer stays.

CONTACT: Carl or Anja
Tel: 01766 515354
info@snowdonlodge.co.uk
www.snowdonlodge.co.uk
Lawrence House, Church Street, Tremadog, Nr Porthmadog, Gwynedd, Snowdonia, LL49 9PS

MAENTWROG
BUNKHOUSE
288a

LLYNDY
BOTHY
288b

Maentwrog bunkhouse is a newly converted cowshed on a working farm. It has a fully equipped kitchen, underfloor heating, TV/DVD, BBQ area, laundry facilities, power washer and bike lockup. Local activities include hill walking (Moelwyn and Cnicht 10 mins away), white water rafting, Coed y Brenin cycling centre, Blaenau Ffestiniog down hill cycle track, RopeWorks & canyoning. Ffestiniog railway and beautiful beaches are within 15-20 mins' drive. The Welsh costal path passes the end of the lane.

Owned by the Llyndy Isaf National Trust Estate, Llyndy Bothy is a simple stone tent providing rustic accommodation.

It is just 15 minutes' walk from the famous Watkin path leading up to the top of Snowdon and 4 miles from Beddgelert.

The bothy has a cold-water tap, sleeping platforms for 6 and an outside toilet. Bring your own camping kit for an off-grid adventure.

DETAILS

- **Open** - All year.
- **Beds** - 4
- **Price/night** - £18pp bring sleeping bags or hire bed linen @£5/person/stay

DETAILS

- **Open** - All year.
- **Beds** - 6: 2x2, 2x1 (sleeping platforms)
- **Price/night** - £30 for whole bothy.

CONTACT: Mrs Eurliw M Jones
Tel: 01766 590231
emj2@hotmail.co.uk
www.bunkhousesnowdonia.com
Felen Rhyd Fach, Maentwrog, Blaenau
Ffestiniog, Gwynedd, LL41 4HY

CONTACT: National Trust Holidays
Tel: 03443 351296
bunkhouses@nationaltrust.org.uk
www.nationaltrust.org.uk/holidays
Llyndy Isaf - National Trust, Llyndy,
Nantgwynant LL55 4NH

CONWY VALLEY
BACKPACKERS BARN

Conwy Valley Backpackers is situated on a peaceful organic farm in the heart of the beautiful Conwy Valley, with excellent access to Snowdonia. Centrally heated with a fully equipped self-catering kitchen, log fires and hot showers. Secure bike/canoe storage. Grazing for horses and tourist information are available. Local activities range from fishing and hiking to white water rafting and mountain biking. Surf Snowdonia is within walking distance and Zip World is a short drive away.

DETAILS

- **Open** - All year. All day.
- **Beds** - 20: 1x4, 1x6 & 1x10
- **Price/night** - From £20pp. Sole use from £275. £3pp bed linen hire.

CONTACT: Claudia
Tel: 01492 660504 or 07956 851425
info@conwyvalleybarn.com
www.conwyvalleybarn.com
Pyllau Gloewon Farm, Tal-y-Bont,
Conwy, Gwynedd, LL32 8YX

BRON-Y-GADER
BUNKHOUSE

Perched at 290m (950ft) in the foothills of Snowdonia with direct access to the Carneddau mountains, Bron-y-Gader Bunkhouse offers comfortable & great value accommodation for up to 37.

Although remote and isolated it is just 8 miles to Conwy and 2 miles to the nearest pub. The many attractions and high adrenaline activities in Snowdonia are just a short drive away.

       GROUPS ONLY

DETAILS

- **Open** - March-Nov. Dec-Feb by prior arrangement
- **Beds** - 37: 4x8, 1x3, 1x2
- **Price/night** - Sole use only: £11pp. Min £110pn. Min stay 2 nights. Discounts for DofE groups

CONTACT:
Tel: 08456 429294
info@bron-y-gader.org
www.bron-y-gader.org
Bron-y-Gader Outdoor Centre, Llanbedr-y-Cennin, Conwy, LL32 8UT

LLANDUDNO
HOSTEL
291

Llandudno Hostel is a Victorian 4* boutique, award-winning hostel where individuals, families & groups (including schools) are welcome all year. Set in the heart of the Victorian seaside town of Llandudno, it's your perfect base for shopping & exploring many local attractions, including blue flag beaches, dry slope skiing, Zip World, Surf Snowdonia, bronze age copper mine, traditional pier, museums & fishing trips.

DETAILS

- **Open** - All year (telephone in winter prior to arrival). All day.
- **Beds** - 46: 2x8,2x6,4x2,1x4,1xfamily(6)
- **Price/night** - From £23 per person, £55 per private twin room, £60 per private twin en suite. Group and family rates on request. Special offers autumn/winter

CONTACT: James or Melissa
Tel: 01492 877430
info@llandudnohostel.co.uk
www.llandudnohostel.co.uk
14 Charlton Street, Llandudno, LL30 2AA

PLATTS FARM
BUNKHOUSE

Platt's Farm Campsite and 3* Bunkhouse is situated in a range of Victorian farm buildings, in the charming village of Llanfairfechan. Close to the A55, the Bunkhouse lies at the start/end of the 14 Welsh 3000 Peaks walks in the Snowdonia National Park, within a 10 min walk of the Wales Coastal Path and on the NCN 5 Cycle Route. Shops, pubs and cafés are within 5 mins' walk. Just 15 mins from Zipworld, Bethesda & 20 mins from Surf Snowdonia.

DETAILS

■ **Open** - All year. Check out before 11am, check in after 2pm.
■ **Beds** - 10
■ **Price/night** - £15.50 pp. Sole use £155 per night.

CONTACT: Sam Davies
Tel: 01248 680105
sam@plattsfarm.com
www.plattsfarm.com
Platts Farm Bunkhouse, Aber Road,
Llanfairfechan, Conwy, LL33 0HL

CABAN CYSGU

GERLAN BUNKHOUSE

Caban Cysgu, run by the community of Gerlan, offers purpose-built accommodation at the foot of the Carneddau. Perfect for walking in Snowdonia, it's a great base for the 'Fourteen 3000ft Peaks' long-distance challenge & The Slate Trail. Just 5 mins from Zip World; the longest and fastest zip line in Europe. There are also plenty of mountain bike trails on the doorstep while road cyclists have the Sustrans route 'Lôn Las Ogwen' just a mile away. For climbers, Idwal is close by, while Afon Ogwen is popular with canoeists.

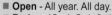

DETAILS

- **Open** - All year. All day.
- **Beds** - 16 : 1x5, 1x2, 1x1, 1x8
- **Price/night** - From £16 - £18

CONTACT: Dewi Emlyn, Manager
Tel: 01248 605573 or 07464 676753
dewi@cabancysgu-gerlan.co.uk
www.cabancysgu-gerlan.co.uk
Ffordd Gerlan, Gerlan, Bethesda,
Bangor, LL57 3ST

SNOWDONIA
MOUNTAIN HOSTEL

294

In the heart of the Ogwen Valley and surrounded by the Welsh 3000s, this hostel is the perfect base for walkers, climbers and cyclists with the best routes straight from the door. For adventure seekers Zip World is within walking distance and the Anglesey Beaches are a short drive. Newly refurbished, Snowdonia Mountain Hostel has comfy beds with linen & a superb kitchen diner.

Sorry no stag or hen parties.

DETAILS
- **Open** - All year (sole use Nov- Mar)
- **Beds** - 26: 2x6, 2x4, 1x4 (self contained flat),1x2
- **Price/night** - From £20

CONTACT: Neil Martinson
Tel: 01248 600416
info@snowdoniamountainhostel.com
www.snowdoniamountainhostel.com
Snowdonia Mountain Hostel, Tai Newyddion, Nant Ffrancon,
Bangor LL57 3DQ

LODGE DINORWIG

On the edge of Snowdonia National Park, Lodge Dinorwig, a former school, has a 14 bed bunkroom. Breakfast is included and evening meals can be booked but there is no self-catering. Perfectly located for all the high adrenaline activities Snowdonia has to offer and with easy access to attractions such as Zip World as well as Snowdon and Llanberis. The on-site café will provide tea and cake after a day in the mountains.

DETAILS

- **Open** - All year. Check in from 3pm, check out by 11am.
- **Beds** - 14: 1x14
- **Price/night** - From £25-£29. Sole use from £300-£350 including breakfast

CONTACT: Simon and Sonni
Tel: 01286 871632
info@lodge-dinorwig.co.uk
www.lodge-dinorwig.co.uk
Dinorwig, Caernarfon,
Gwynedd, LL55 3EY

OLD SCHOOL
LODGE

In the small mountain village of Deiniolen, in the heart of Snowdonia, not far from Llanberis, The Old School Lodge is the perfect base for groups of all kinds wishing to explore the rugged splendour of North Wales. Perfect for groups of walkers or climbers, the Lodge provides high quality accommodation for those looking for a warm comfortable base to return to after a day on the Welsh mountains. Facilities include a well equipped self-catering kitchen, lounge, games room & resources room.

       GROUPS ONLY

DETAILS

- **Open** - All year. All day.
- **Beds** - 38: 1x6,7x4,2x2
- **Price/night** - £19pp. Scouts and Guides: £14.25. Minimum stay 2 nights, minimum charge based on 12 people.

CONTACT: Booking Secretary
Tel: 01516 324943
activities@oldschoollodge.org.uk
www.oldschoollodge.org.uk
Deiniolen, Caernarfon LL55 3HH

ARETE
OUTDOOR CENTRE
297

The Arete Outdoor Centre, in Snowdonia National Park, offers excellent access to the stunning coastline, mountains & lakes of North Wales and Anglesey. With comfortable, affordable, bunkhouse accommodation and large kitchens this is a great base for groups of friends or family. The team can advise on how best to spend your stay and a range of exciting outdoor activities are available through the centre's well qualified staff.

GROUPS ONLY

DETAILS

- **Open** - All year. All day.
- **Beds** - 100+ in 22 rooms split into three blocks of 20, 58 and 30+
- **Price/night** - Catered from £30pp, self-catering from £15 pp. Sole use deals.

CONTACT: Gareth Davies
Tel: 01286 672136
info@aretecentre.co.uk
www.aretecentre.co.uk
Arete Outdoor Education Centre,
Llanrug, Caernarfon,
Gwynedd, LL55 4AP

PENTRE BACH
BUNKHOUSE

298

Situated between Waunfawr and Betws Garmon, Pentre Bach Bunkhouse provides dog friendly accommodation, outdoor activities and a campsite. The ground floor of the bunkhouse has a dining/cooking area while upstairs there are alpine sleeping platforms with mattresses for 16. Showers, toilets and washing/drying facilities, shared with the campsite, are just across the yard.

DETAILS

- **Open** - All year. All day. Enquires 9am - 10pm. Arrive from 4pm, leave by 11am.
- **Beds** - 16: 1x16.
- **Price/night** - Prices: £14pp (inc gas, electric & showers). Sole use bookings negotiable according to group size.

CONTACT: Karen Neil
Tel: 01286 650643 (5-10pm) or 07798 733939 (9am-5pm)
info@bachventures.co.uk
www.pentrebachbunkhouse.co.uk
Pentre Bach, Waunfawr, Caernarfon, Gwynedd, LL54 7AJ

RHYD DDU
OUTDOOR CENTRE

The Rhyd Ddu Bunkhouse provides group accommodation at the foot of Snowdon and the Nantlle Ridge. Sleeping 30 in 6 bedrooms, it has a fully equipped kitchen and a large communal dining room with a big screen - great for movie nights! Glorious views, central heating, fast WiFi, parking, secure bike storage, drying room and a large garden. Bring your own sleeping bag, pillow case and towel. A pub, café, and steam train station are all within 2 minutes' walk.

DETAILS

- **Open** - All year. All day. Check in from 4pm, check out by 11am.
- **Beds** - 30: 1x12, 4x4, 1x2
- **Price/night** - Sole use from £275 per night. Minimum stay of 2 nights. 4 nights for the price of 3 available.

CONTACT: Robat
Tel: 01286 882688
stay@canolfan-rhyd-ddu.cymru
www.snowdonia-bunkhouse.wales
Rhyd Ddu, Snowdonia, Wales LL54 6TL

BRYNKIR
COACH HOUSE

Reopening in spring 2020 after refurbishment. Formerly known as Cwm Pennant Hostel, Brynkir Coach House offers welcoming & relaxed accommodation for groups of 24-63. Adventure activities can be provided. Home-made ready meals & packed lunches available. Set within stunning grounds in the Snowdonia National Park with fantastic views of the Cwm Pennant valley & Moel Hebog.

 GROUPS ONLY

DETAILS

- **Open** - Opening spring 2020.
- **Beds** - 63: 1x15 (en-suite), 1x14, 1x7, 1x9, 1x6 (family en-suite), 2x3 (family en-suite), 1x6 (self-contained flat)
- **Price/night** - £17.50pp. Min stay 2 nights. Min fee £840

CONTACT: Dawn Harding
Tel: 01766 549321 or 07866 631538
dawnharding14@icloud.com
www.cwmpennanthostel.com
Golan, Garndolbenmaen,
Gwynedd, LL51 9AQ

ABERSOCH
SGUBOR UNNOS
301

Bunkhouse accommodation on a family farm in the village of Llangian. Just one mile from Abersoch which is famed for watersports, the bunkhouse is an ideal base for walking the Llyn Coast Path, surfing, cycling, golf, fishing, running & sailing. Spinning & knitting courses using the farm's own wool are available. The three modern bunkrooms are ideal for individuals or groups with a fully equipped kitchen/lounge, disabled facilities, secure storage & parking.

DETAILS
- **Open** - All year. All day.
- **Beds** - 14: 2x4, 1x6
- **Price/night** - £20 (adult), £10 (under 10 years), including a light breakfast and bed linen. Discount for 3+ nights.

CONTACT: Phil or Meinir
Tel: 01758 713527
enquiries@tanrallt.com
www.tanrallt.com
Fferm Tanrallt Farm, Llangian, Abersoch, Gwynedd, LL53 7LN

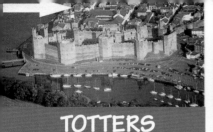

TOTTERS

302a

ANGLESEY
OUTDOOR CENTRE

302b

Totters sits in the heart of the historic castle town of Caernarfon just 30m from the Menai Straits. Close to many pubs and restaurants but with good public transport to the Snowdonia National Park. The hostel is a 200 year old, five floored town house with five bedrooms sleeping either 4 or 6 and a huge double/family en suite. Opposite there is a self-catering town house sleeping 6.

Anglesey Outdoors is an ideal base for groups, individuals or families. It is just a mile from Porthdafarch Beach & the coastal path and only 2km from Sustrans Cycle Route 8. It has four self contained areas each with their own self-catering & bathroom facilities. These can be hired individually or together. Full catering an option and there's an on-site bar/bistro. Yurts and cabans also available.

DETAILS	DETAILS

- **Open** - All year. All day. Check in by 10 pm.
- **Beds** - 28: 3x6, 2x4, 1x2 (en suite), 1x2 (twin)
- **Price/night** - £19.50pp in a dorm. £55 for a double/twin en suite. £47.50 for a twin. Discounts for groups.

CONTACT: Bob/Henryette
Tel: 01286 672963 or 07979 830470
totters.hostel@gmail.com
www.totters.co.uk
Plas Porth Yr Aur, 2 High Street,
Caernarfon, Gwynedd, LL55 1RN

- **Open** - All year. 24 hour access.
- **Beds** - 68: Main Centre 33: 1x7,4x5,1x4,1x2. Maris Annexe 10: 5x2. Ty Pen Annexe 8: 1x4,2x2. Gogarth Dorms 16: 1x7,1x7,1x2.
- **Price/night** - £12pp (Gogarth Dorms) to £24pp ensuite twin. Ask about sole use.

CONTACT: Penny Hurndall
Tel: 01407 769351
penny@angleseyoutdoors.com
www.angleseyoutdoors.com
Porthdafarch Road, Holyhead,
Anglesey, LL65 2LP

OUTDOOR
ALTERNATIVE

303

This purpose built 4* centre is quietly tucked away in Rhoscolyn, an Area of Outstanding Natural Beauty on the Anglesey Coast. Just 5 mins' walk to the sandy beach at Borthwen and a stone's throw from the Anglesey Coastal Path. Perfect for friends & families, outdoor groups, schools and universities. Your ideal base for kayaking, climbing, sailing, walking, bird watching or beach holidays.
Careful energy use is encouraged, with composting and recycling. Nearby Holyhead has ferry links to Ireland.

DETAILS

- **Open** - All year. 24 hour access.
- **Beds** - 20: 2x2, 1x4, 2x6. 20: 1x3, 3x4, 1x5.
- **Price/night** - £24pp. £410 for sole use.

CONTACT: Jacqui Short
Tel: 01407 860469
enquiries@outdooralternative.co.uk
www.outdooralternative.co.uk
Cerrig-yr-Adar, Rhoscolyn, Holyhead,
Anglesey, LL65 2NQ

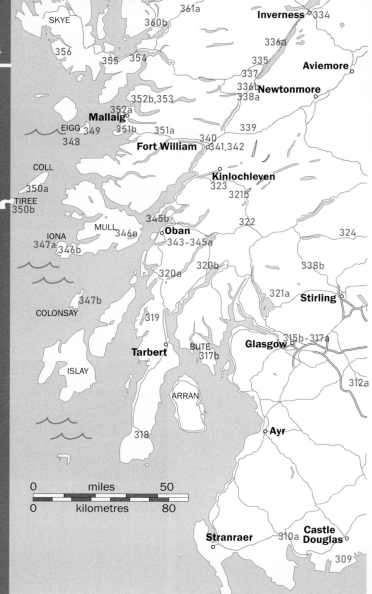

SKYE

361a

Inverness ○ 334

360b

336a

356

355 354

335

Aviemore ○

337

336b

Newtonmore ○

352b,353

338a

352a

Mallaig ○

Fort William

351b 351a

349

EIGG

348

339

340

341,342

Kinlochleven ○

323

321b

COLL

350a

322

324

TIREE

350b

MULL

345b

Oban ○

343-345a

IONA

346a

338b

347a 346b

320b

COLONSAY

347b

320a

321a

Stirling ○

319

315b-317a

Glasgow ○

Tarbert ○

BUTE

317b

312a

ISLAY

ARRAN

0 miles 50

0 kilometres 80

318

Ayr ○

Stranraer ○

310a

Castle Douglas ○

309

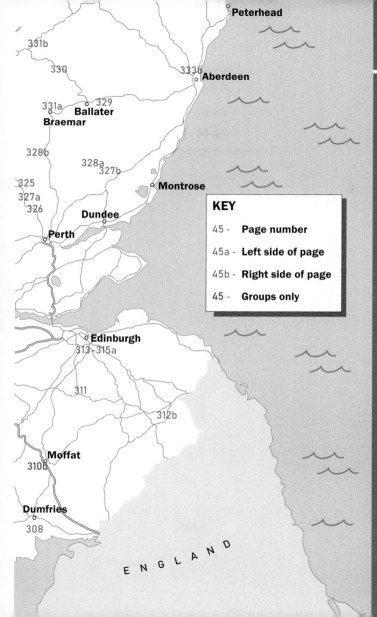

South Scotland

Peterhead

331b

330

333b Aberdeen

331a 329
Ballater
Braemar

328b

328a
327b

325
327a
326

Montrose

Dundee

Perth

KEY

45 -   **Page number**

45a -   **Left side of page**

45b -   **Right side of page**

45 -   **Groups only**

Edinburgh
313 - 315a

311

312b

Moffat
310b

Dumfries
308

ENGLAND

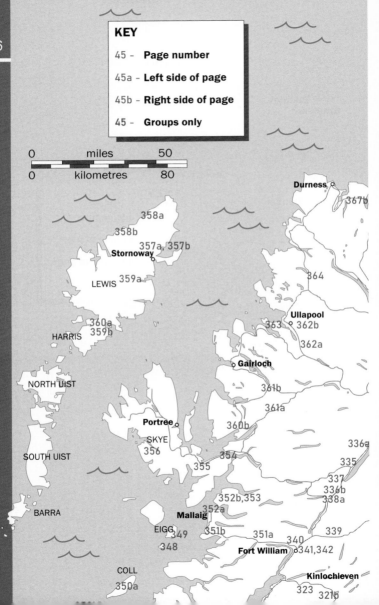

North Scotland

KEY

45 - **Page number**

45a - **Left side of page**

45b - **Right side of page**

45 - **Groups only**

0   miles   50

0   kilometres   80

Durness

367b

358a

358b

357a, 357b

Stornoway

LEWIS

359a

364

Ullapool

363   362b

362a

360a

359b

HARRIS

Gairloch

NORTH UIST

361b

361a

Portree

SKYE

356

360b

354

336a

335

355

337

336b

338a

352b,353

352a

Mallaig

EIGG

349

351b

351a

340

339

348

Fort William 341,342

BARRA

SOUTH UIST

COLL

350a

Kinlochleven

323   321b

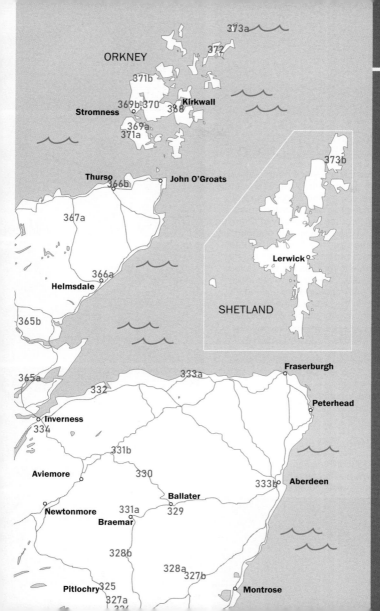

ORKNEY

373a

372

371b

369b 370 368 Kirkwall

Stromness

369a

371a

Thurso

John O'Groats

366b

373b

367a

Lerwick

366a

Helmsdale

365b

SHETLAND

333a

Fraserburgh

365a

332

Peterhead

Inverness

334

331b

Aviemore

330

333b Aberdeen

Newtonmore

331a 329

Ballater

Braemar

328b

328a 327b

Pitlochry 325

Montrose

327a

324

MARTHROWN
OF MABIE

Marthrown is set in the heart of Mabie Forest, 6 miles south of Dumfries. It has a sauna, a wood burning spring water hot tub, a large BBQ, garden areas, a challenge course and plenty of room for groups. There are a variety of mountain bike routes and the 7Stanes mountain bike trails are nearby. Catered meals available for groups. As well as the bunkhouse, there are also Mongolian yurts, an American style tipi and the jewel in the crown is the Iron Age Roundhouse for parties or weddings.

DETAILS

- **Open** - All year. 24 hours - late arrival by arrangement.
- **Beds** - 26: 1x8,1x7,1x6,1x5 + Roundhouse, 2 Yurts, Tipi and camping.
- **Price/night** - £18 to £21.50.

CONTACT: Mike or Pam Hazlehurst
Tel: 01387 247900
info@marthrownofmabie.co.uk
www.marthrownofmabie.co.uk
Mabie Forest, Dumfries, DG2 8HB

CASTLE CREAVIE
HAY BARN HOSTEL

This comfortable family friendly hostel sleeps 6. It is set on a working farm and is surrounded by spectacular Galloway countryside. The hugely spacious open plan design has oak floors, comfy beds, dining area, wood burning stove, separate kitchen with basic cooking facilities, washroom & W.C.

There are also: hot showers, washing/ drying facilities, bike wash and store. Breakfast and farm produce available. The ideal base for walkers and cyclists with 7Stanes and NCN Route 7 close by.

        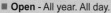

DETAILS
- **Open** - All year. All day.
- **Beds** - 6: 1x4, 1x2
- **Price/night** - £20pp bed linen provided & beds made up. Electricity included.

CONTACT: Charlie and Elaine Wannop
Tel: 01557 500238
elaine@castlecreavie.co.uk
www.castlecreavie.co.uk
Castle Creavie, Kirkcudbright, DG6 4QE

BARHOLM
ACCOMMODATION
310a

310b
WELL ROAD
CENTRE

Barholm Enterprise Centre houses a variety of businesses including an Arts and Crafts Co-operative and Barholm Accommodation which has en suite shared and private rooms.

Perfect for cyclists, walkers, fishermen or those who generally enjoy the outdoors. Facilities include a communal kitchenette (fridge/freezer, kettle, toaster and microwave), sitting room, on-site cycle hire and bike repair facilities & electric car charging.

The Well Road Centre sits in its own grounds in the charming town of Moffat. It is ideal for all types of groups, conferences, residential workshops, sports, social events and outdoor activity clubs. The Centre has two spacious meeting rooms, a large bright self-catering kitchen, dining room fully equipped for 65, games hall for indoor activities and table tennis room. Bring your own sleeping bags or linens for single duvets. Ample parking & storage.

DETAILS
- **Open** - All year. All day
- **Beds** - 28
- **Price/night** - From £20

DETAILS
- **Open** - All year. All day.
- **Beds** - 70: in 13 rooms (2 en suite).
- **Price/night** - From £830 for two nights mid week for up to 30 people. £25 pp for 31+ . From £975 for two nights weekend for up to 35 people. £25pp for 36+.

CONTACT: Jenny Adams
Tel: 01671 820810
jenny.barholm@gmail.com
barholm-centre.co.uk
St Johns Street, Creetown, Dumfries and Galloway, DG8 7JE

CONTACT: Ben Larmour
Tel: 01683 221040
Ben8363@aol.com
www.wellroadcentre.com
Well Road Centre, Moffat, DG10 9BT

CLEIKUM MILL
LODGE

Cleikum Mill Lodge is a modernised character building in the heart of the Tweed Valley. The Mill sleeps 12, 8 in the Lower Mill and 4 in the Upper Mill. Book individual rooms, a floor or the whole Mill. Innerleithen, a 7Stanes trail centre, is on the NCR1 and Southern Upland Way. It has shops, pubs, restaurants and cafés a short stroll away Dog friendly if booking the whole building in advance.

DETAILS

- **Open** - All year. All day. Check in after 4pm, check out before 10am.
- **Beds** - 12: Lower:1x2,2x3. Upper: 2x2
- **Price/night** - £35 single, £56 twin, £73 triple room. Apartment for four £112. Discounts for 3 nights or more. The longer you stay the higher the discount.

CONTACT: Graham
Tel: 07790 592747
hello@cleikum-mill-lodge.co.uk
www.cleikum-mill-lodge.co.uk
7 Cleikum Mill, High St, Innerleithen,
Scottish Borders EH44 6QT

WEE ROW
HOSTEL
312a

KIRK YETHOLM
FRIENDS OF NATURE
312b

Located in the heart of New Lanark World Heritage Site and just one hour's drive from either Glasgow or Edinburgh, Wee Row is the perfect base for your holiday. The award winning New Lanark Visitor Centre is on the doorstep; step back in time and rediscover life in this working mill village. The hostel sleeps 62 in 18 private rooms (all en suite) and has terrific views over the River Clyde and surrounding countryside. Facilities include bike storage, laundry and drying room. Breakfasts and evening meals are available at the New Lanark Mill Hotel.

Kirk Yetholm Friends of Nature House is perfectly located at the start/end of the Pennine Way. It is also close to St. Cuthbert's Way, the Borderloop Cycle Route and Sustrans Route 84. It's a great base too for local day hikes, ideal for individuals, families and small groups. Recently upgraded, the house offers a comfortable, friendly and peaceful retreat. Evening meals and breakfast are available in the adjacent hotel.

DETAILS
- **Open** - March- End November
- **Beds** - 62: 6x2, 1x3, 3x3, 8x4 +Studio
- **Price/night** - From £19.50 per person

DETAILS
- **Open** - All year (Nov-Feb groups only). Reception 5pm-11pm & 8am-10am.
- **Beds** - 22: 1x7, 1x5, 1x4, 2x2 (twin), 1x2 (bunk).
- **Price/night** - From £20, under 18's from £17. Discounts for IFN / SYHA / HI.

CONTACT: Reception
Tel: 01555 666710
weerowhostel@newlanark.org
www.newlanarkhostel.co.uk
Wee Row Hostel, Wee Row, New Lanark, Lanark, Lanarkshire, ML11 9DJ

CONTACT: The Manager
Tel: 01573 420639
kirkyetholm@thefriendsofnature.org.uk
www.thefriendsofnature.org.uk
Friends of Nature House ,Waukford, Kirk Yetholm, Kelso,Roxburghshire, TD5 8PG

EURO HOSTEL
EDINBURGH HALLS
313

During the Summer and Festival, Euro Hostel Edinburgh Halls offers you choice and comfort at budget friendly prices.

Apartments for 3 - 12, private twin and single rooms. Perfect for any event in Edinburgh, sports fans, hen/stag parties and backpackers. Five mins walk from the Grassmarket. Open June, July and August. Continental Breakfast £5.

DETAILS
- **Open** - June, July & August only. Check-in from 3pm. Check-out by 11am
- **Beds** - 383: in single/twin rooms within shared apartments. Private apartments are available for groups of 3 - 12 people.
- **Price/night** - From £20pp. Continental breakfast bag (takeaway) £5.

CONTACT: The Reservations Team
Tel: 0845 490 0461
edinburgh@eurohostels.co.uk
www.eurohostels.co.uk/edinburgh
Kincaids Court, Guthrie Street,
Edinburgh, EH1 1JT

ROYAL MILE
BACKPACKERS
314a

CASTLE ROCK
HOSTEL
314b

Royal Mile Backpackers is a small and cosy hostel with its own special character! Perfectly located on the Royal Mile, the most famous street in Edinburgh, Royal Mile Backpackers is the ideal place to stay for the independent traveller.

The comfortable beds and cosy common areas will make you feel at home and the friendly staff are always on hand to help you make the most of your time in Edinburgh.

In a wonderful location, facing south with a sunny aspect and panoramic views over the city, Castle Rock Hostel is just steps away from the city centre. The historic Royal Mile, the busy pubs, the late-late nightlife of Grassmarket and Cowgate are all only a short walk away. Then, of course, there is the famous Edinburgh Castle.

Most of the rooms have no traffic noise and there are loads of great facilities, 24-hour reception and no curfew.

DETAILS
■ **Open** - All year. Reception 6.30am - 3am (24 hrs during August).
■ **Beds** - 46
■ **Price/night** - From £10 per person. ID required for check in.

CONTACT: Receptionist
Tel: 0131 557 6120
royalmile@scotlandstophostels.com
www.royalmilebackpackers.com
105 High Street, Edinburgh, EH1 1SG

DETAILS
■ **Open** - All year. Reception 24 hours.
■ **Beds** - 302
■ **Price/night** - From £14 per person. ID required for check in.

CONTACT: Receptionist
Tel: 0131 225 9666
castlerock@macbackpackers.com
www.castlerockedinburgh.com
15 Johnston Terrace,
Edinburgh, EH1 2PW

HIGH STREET
HOSTEL

315a

315b

BLYTHSWOOD
HOUSE

The High Street Hostel is one of Europe's best regarded and most atmospheric hostels. It is hugely popular with world travellers. Located just off the historic Royal Mile in a 470 year old building, it is your perfect base for exploring all the city's many attractions and of course its wonderful nightlife.

Providing excellence in location, ambience and facilities, the hostel is highly recommended by more than ten of the world's top backpacker travel guides. Come along and see for yourself!

In the heart of Glasgow city centre. Blythswood House is the perfect base from which to explore everything the city has to offer. The single rooms are grouped in flats of 2,6,7 or 8 so perfect for individuals or groups wanting to visit Glasgow in the summer. All rooms are en suite and each flat has self-catering facilities. Easily accessible from the city's train and bus stations Blythswood House welcomes walkers and cyclists.

DETAILS

- **Open** - All year. All day.
- **Beds** - 156
- **Price/night** - From £14 per person. ID required for check in.

CONTACT: Reception
Tel: 0131 557 3984
highstreethostel@macbackpackers.com
www.highstreethostel.com
8 Blackfriars St., Edinburgh, EH1 1NE

DETAILS

- **Open** - June - Early September
- **Beds** - 170 single rooms within flats 2, 6, 7, or 8 some doubles available.
- **Price/night** - Individual £38, £230pp per week, Student discounts available. 15% reduction for 6+ people

CONTACT: Rebecca Forsyth
Tel: 0141 566 1121
accommodation@gsa.ac.uk
www.gsa.ac.uk/visit-gsa/summer-accommodation
200 West Regent Street, Glasgow, G2 4DQ

EURO HOSTEL
GLASGOW
316

Glasgow city centre budget accommodation in mix of en suite private rooms, dorms and VIP suites for groups of 1-20. All rooms are en-suite with mobile cable charging stations. Free superfast WiFi. Perfect for shopping, sports events, gigs & exhibitions. Ideal for individuals & groups. Enjoy 'All You Can Eat' buffet breakfasts (£5pp), meal deals and drink promos in the bar. Just 5 mins from Central Station.

DETAILS

■ **Open** - All year. 24 hr reception. Check in from 3pm.
■ **Beds** - 452: in en suite private rooms, dorms and VIP suites for groups.
■ **Price/night** - Beds from £10. Rooms from £20. VIP suites from £14pp. Book direct for Best Price Guarantee.

CONTACT: The Reservations Team
Tel: 0845 539 9956
glasgow@eurohostels.co.uk
www.eurohostels.co.uk/glasgow
318 Clyde Street, Glasgow, G1 4NR

TARTAN
LODGE
317a

BUTE
BACKPACKERS
317b

On Alexandra Parade, near Denistoun and 20 minutes' walk from Glasgow city centre, Tartan Lodge, is set within a former 19th century church and Masonic Lodge. You will find affordable accommodation for budget and business travellers with a selection of double and twin en suite bedrooms and shared dormitories with family facilities. Towels can be hired.

Bute Backpackers is a well established 4* hostel, located on the seafront of Rothesay, Isle of Bute. It accommodates up to 45 people in 14 bedrooms (single/twin/double/family, some en suite). The main house has a sea front sun lounge with TV, free WiFi, a fully equipped self-catering kitchen & a laundry room. There are regular live music sessions & open mic nights. Plenty of free on street parking and a secure bike shed.

DETAILS
- **Open** - All year. Check in from 2pm. Check out by 11am
- **Beds** - 93: 5 x double, 2 x twin, 1 x triple. Dorms: 2x3, 8x4, 1x4 female, 2x6, 1x6 female, 2x8
- **Price/night** - Dorms from £10pp. Private rooms from £50 per room

DETAILS
- **Open** - All year. 24hr access, no curfew. Reception 9am - 10pm
- **Beds** - 45 beds: 14 bedrooms; 4 family rooms, 4 twin rooms, 6 bunk rooms.
- **Price/night** - £20pp dorm, £22.50pp twin, £25pp single.

CONTACT: Reception
Tel: 0141 554 5970
info@tartanlodge.co.uk
www.tartanlodge.co.uk
235 Alexandra Parade, Glasgow, G31 3AW

CONTACT: Reception
Tel: 01700 501876
butebackpackers@hotmail.com
www.butebackpackers.co.uk
The Pier View, 36 Argyle Street, Rothesay, Isle of Bute, PA20 0AX

CAMPBELTOWN
BACKPACKERS

318

The Campbeltown Backpackers is housed in the Old Schoolhouse, a Grade B listed building.

The hostel offers easy access to the facilities of Campbeltown including swimming pool, gym, cinema and distillery tours. It is a good stop along the Kintyre Way which gives walkers spectacular views of the surrounding islands. The area also enjoys very good windsurfing, surfing, mountain bike routes and other major cycle trails.

DETAILS
- **Open** - All year. Leave by 10.30am on day of departure.
- **Beds** - 16: 1x6, 1x10
- **Price/night** - £22 per person

CONTACT: Alan
Tel: 01586 551188
info@campbeltownbackpackers.co.uk
campbeltownbackpackers.co.uk
Kintyre Amenity Trust, Big Kiln,
Campbeltown, Argyll, PA28 6JF

ARGYLL
BACKPACKERS

If you enjoy spectacular views and watching wildlife in modern comfortable self-catering accommodation then you'll love Argyll Backpackers! Located on the banks of Loch Fyne, just minutes from Cycle Route 78 in the hamlet of Inverneil, it's perfect for island hopping to Arran and Islay. You'll be able to stock up on supplies from Tarbert or Ardrishaig / Lochgilphead, depending on your route.

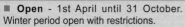

DETAILS

- **Open** - 1st April until 31 October. Winter period open with restrictions.
- **Beds** - 24: 1x2(dbl), 1x3(dbl+bunk), 2x2,1x4 ensuite,1x5 ensuite,1x6 ensuite.
- **Price/night** - £24pp (£23pp if 3 nights or more). Sole use: From £480pn. Enquire for weddings, Xmas & New Year.

CONTACT: Pam Richmond
Tel: 01546 603366 Mobile:07786 157727
argyllbackpackers@sky.com
www.argyllbackpackers.com
Loch Fyne Lodge, Inverneil, Ardrishaig, Argyll, PA30 8ES

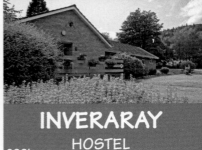

TORRAN BAY
HOSTEL
320a

INVERARAY
HOSTEL
320b

With 16 en suite rooms, Torran Bay Hostel lies at the southern end of Loch Awe. A perfect base for your holiday.

Enjoy excellent fishing or launch your boat from Torran Farm land and spend the day on the 25 mile long loch. Other activities include hiking, cycling, bird watching or golf. Prices includes continental breakfast and all rooms have TV and DVD.

The historic town of Inveraray, on the western shore of Loch Fyne, is a superb location for exploring Scotland's Southern Highlands and Islands.

Inverarary Hostel is perfect for independent holidaymakers who enjoy socialising. The hostel offers simple, comfortable accommodation in private rooms & shared dorms, an excellent self-catering kitchen, communal dining area and a cosy wee lounge.

DETAILS
- **Open** - All year. All day.
- **Beds** - 34: 10x2 or double, 2 x double and single, 1x4 , 2x3
- **Price/night** - From £50 to £72 per room, including continental breakfast and parking. Group bookings welcome..

DETAILS
- **Open** - Late Mar-early Oct. Reception 8-10am/3.30-9.30pm. No daytime access.
- **Beds** - 21 in 10 rooms
- **Price/night** - From £19.50pp. Breakfast £3.90

CONTACT: Sheila Brolly
Tel: 01546 810133
sheilabro1@hotmail.co.uk
www.torranbayhostel.co.uk
Torran Farm, Ford, Lochgilphead.
PA31 8RH

CONTACT: Dawn or Ruben
Tel: 01499 302454
info@inverarayhostel.co.uk
www.inverarayhostel.co.uk
Dalmally Road, Inveraray,
Argyll, PA32 8XD

BALMAHA
BUNKHOUSE / HOSTEL

321a

KINGSHOUSE
BUNKHOUSE

321b

CLOSED UNTIL FURTHER NOTICE. On the banks of Loch Lomond on the West Highland Way, Balmaha Bunkhouse offered quality accommodation with breakfast, bedding, WiFi, tea & coffee included. Ideal for walkers and family get-togethers. A private self-catering chalet slept 4 and there was B&B (en suite) in the main house. Kayaks and Canadian canoes were available for hire on site.

Within the grounds of the famous Kingshouse Hotel, this brand new, purpose built bunkhouse is right on the West Highland Way amid spectacular Scottish mountain scenery. With 32 beds across 10 rooms there is ample storage. Each each bunk has a locker, reading light, power socket, linen & towels. Ideal for travellers needing a stop-over or as a base to explore Glencoe and beyond.

You'll find skiing, walking & mountain biking on the doorstep. The Way Inn café offers all day dining & packed lunches. Open from 7.30am to 9pm daily.

DETAILS

- **Open** - Arrive 2pm-7pm, leave by 10am
- **Beds** - Bunkhouse 14: 1x6,1x4 (family),1x2 (double/twin),1x2 (twin); The Roost 4: 1x4; B&B: 1xdbl,1xtwin,1x single.
- **Price/night** - From £25pp. Chalet £90. Dog £5pn. B&B (hot breakfast): Dbl £80, twin £80, single £35/40.

DETAILS

- **Open** - All year.
- **Beds** - 32: 1x6, 4x4, 5x2
- **Price/night** - From £35 per person.

CONTACT: Reception
Tel: 01536 763352
info@ariespensions.co.uk
www.balmaha-bunkhouse.co.uk
Balmaha, Loch Lomond, G63 0JQ

CONTACT:
Tel: 01855 851259
contact@kingshousehotel.co.uk
www.kingshousehotel.co.uk
Glencoe, Argyll, PH49 4HY

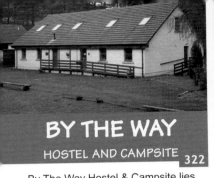

BY THE WAY

HOSTEL AND CAMPSITE

322

By The Way Hostel & Campsite lies in the Loch Lomond National Park between Arrochar's peaks & Glencoe. There's excellent walking, climbing and white water rafting. The accommodation includes camping, various huts: hobbit houses, posh pods, glamping & trekker huts, camping cabins & a purpose built 4* hostel with twin, double & dormitory rooms, with great self-catering facilities. For more comfort still there are 2 chalets; one with three bedrooms, one with two.

        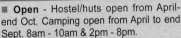

DETAILS

■ **Open** - Hostel/huts open from April-end Oct. Camping open from April to end Sept. 8am - 10am & 2pm - 8pm.
■ **Beds** - 26 hostel; 36 huts; 50 camping.
■ **Price/night** - Hostel dorms from £20pp. Huts vary. Camping £8pp.

CONTACT: Kirsty Burnett
Tel: 01838 400333
info@TyndrumByTheWay.com
www.TyndrumByTheWay.com
Lower Station Rd, Tyndrum, FK20 8RY

GLENCOE
INDEPENDENT HOSTEL

Glencoe Independent Hostel lies in secluded woodland midway between Glencoe village and Clachaig Inn with access to world class cycling, walking, climbing and kayaking. The Glencoe Ski Centre and The West Highland Way are just 20 mins away. The hostel has 4 rooms with comfortable communal spaces. Also available are an alpine bunkhouse sleeping 16, 4 luxury caravans and 3 luxury log cabins.

DETAILS

- **Open** - All year (phone in Nov and Dec). 9am - 9 pm.
- **Beds** - 65: hostel:26, bunkhouse:16, caravans: 4x2-4, cabins: 2x2, 1x3
- **Price/night** - From £13.50 to £50 per person.

CONTACT: Keith or Davina
Tel: 01855 811906
info@glencoehostel.co.uk
www.glencoehostel.co.uk
Glencoe Independent Hostel, Glencoe, Argyll, PH49 4HX

COMRIE
CROFT

324

Comrie Croft is a perfect rural retreat for mountain bikers, hikers, families & backpackers, just over an hour from Edinburgh & Glasgow. The 4* hostel offers cosy, home style rooms which are also available for sole use & weddings.

On-site facilities include café, bike shop, lots of mountain bike trails, family-friendly valley routes and a farm shop. A footpath takes you to the vibrant village of Comrie & gives access to stunning glens and mountains.

DETAILS

- **Open** - All year. All day.
- **Beds** - 58 + 16
- **Price/night** - Standard room: £20pp. En suite room: £22pp. Children 5 - 17yrs: 1/2 price. Under 5's: Free

CONTACT:
Tel: 01764 670140
info@comriecroft.com
www.comriecroft.com
Comrie Croft, By Crieff/Comrie,
Perthshire, PH7 4JZ

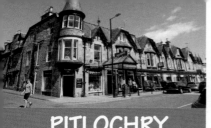

PITLOCHRY
BACKPACKERS HOTEL

325

Located in the centre of beautiful Pitlochry, this friendly, cosy hostel is an old Victorian hotel literally bursting with character and provides dormitory and en suite private rooms. Comfy beds come with fitted sheets, duvets and 2 fluffy pillows and private rooms have fresh towels. The bright spacious lounge has comfy sofas and as many free hot drinks as you can drink. There's free WiFi, games, musical instruments and a free pool table. A great place to meet like minded people. You won't want to leave!

DETAILS

■ **Open** - March to Nov. 7.30am-1pm and 5pm-10pm (times may vary).
■ **Beds** - 79
■ **Price/night** - From £18pp for dorms. Private rooms from £25pp

CONTACT: Receptionist
Tel: 01796 470044
info@pitlochrybackpackershotel.com
www.pitlochrybackpackershotel.com
134 Atholl Road, Pitlochry, PH16 5AB

JESSIE MACS

In the centre of Birnam just 10 mins' walk from Dunkeld, this refurbished Victorian manse offers a mix of self-catering hostel and B&B accommodation. Your perfect base to discover the mountains, waters, rich culture and heritage of Big Tree Country. Jessie Mac's has doubles, bunk rooms and family rooms, all en suite. One double has wheelchair access.

DETAILS

■ **Open** - All year. Check in: 4-6.30pm. Check out: by 10am.
■ **Beds** - 21: 4x2, 2x4, 1x5
■ **Price/night** - Dorm £22pp +continental breakfast £27, +cooked breakfast £30. Double £29.50pp (based on 2 sharing) or £35 single occ. Child £11 in shared room. Infants free. Group rates available.

CONTACT: Dot Mechan
Tel: 01350 727324
info@jessiemacs.co.uk
www.jessiemacs.co.uk
Murthly Terrace, Birnam, Dunkeld PH8 0BG

TAY BUNKHOUSE

327a

AUCHLISHIE
BUNKHOUSE

327b

Tay Bunkhouse, on the banks of the river Tay in Highland Perthshire, is a stone cottage stylishly renovated to provide comfotable accommodation for groups up to 12. It has a fully equipped self catering kitchen, a comfy lounge and dining area, freshly laundered beds and free WiFi. The garden has a BBQ, fire pit and outdoor seating, with riverside access for canoes. Dogs are welcome by arrangement.

A brand new family owned bunkhouse situated in Kirriemuir, at the gateway to the Glens of Isla, Prosen and Clova.

The bunkhouse offers excellent facilities to the outdoor enthusiast wanting to experience and enjoy the proximity to the Cairngorms National Park.

An architect designed, purpose built bunkhouse with full kitchen, shower and drying room facilities. Cosy duvets, pillows and bed linen provided, towels available to hire.

DETAILS

■ **Open** - All year. Groups only Apr-Oct weekends.
■ **Beds** - 12: 1x2, 1x4, 1x6
■ **Price/night** - Winter from £120, Apr-Oct from £175, for sole use of whole bunkhouse. Two nights minimum stay. Please enquire for smaller groups.

CONTACT: George or Ben
Tel: 07565 542 766
info@taybunkhouse.co.uk
taybunkhouse.co.uk
The Old Post Office, Logierait PH9 0LH

DETAILS

■ **Open** - All year
■ **Beds** - 24
■ **Price/night** - From £25 per person

CONTACT: James or Nicky
Tel: 07867 476300
james.helyer@auchlishie.co.uk
www.auchlishie-bunkhouse.co.uk
Auchlishie Farm, Kirriemuir,
Angus DD8 4LS

PROSEN
HOSTEL
328a

GULABIN
LODGE
328b

Glenprosen is the most intimate of the Angus Glens on the southernmost edge of the Cairngorms National Park. Two Munros; the Mayar and Driesh link Glenprosen to the Cairngorms plateau. Prosen Hostel is also close to the upgraded East Cairngorms footpath network. Converted to the latest and greenest specification, the 4* hostel offers cosy, quality accommodation for 18. With 4 rooms, sleeping 4, 4 and 6 in bunks and a family room sleeping 4. You can also hire the nearby village hall.

Gulabin Lodge nestles in Glenshee at the foot of Beinn Gulabin and is the nearest accommodation to the Glenshee ski slopes. The 4* lodge offers excellent accommodation for individuals, families, stag and hen groups & school residentials. On-site there are many outdoor activities including mountain bike hire. During the winter there's a ski school with equipment hire. Meals & transport to and from airports /stations available for groups. A 12/14 bed house is also available.

DETAILS

- **Open** - All year. All day.
- **Beds** - 18:1x6, 3x4
- **Price/night** - £23 pp. Min periods & prices apply for Xmas and New Year.

CONTACT: Hector or Robert
Tel: 01575 540302
hectormaclean@compuserve.com
www.prosenhostel.co.uk
Prosen Hostel, Balnaboth, Kirriemuir, Angus, DD8 4SA

DETAILS

- **Open** - All year. 24 hours.
- **Beds** - 40: 9 rooms available.
- **Price/night** - From £20pp. Contact for fully catered stays and private rooms.

CONTACT: Darren and Tereza
Tel: 01250 885255/ 07799 847014
info@gulabinlodge.co.uk
www.gulabinoutdoors.co.uk
Spittal of Glenshee, By Blairgowrie, PH10 7QE

BALLATER
HOSTEL

329

Ballater Hostel lies in the centre of Ballater, near Balmoral, on the east side of the Cairngorms National Park. Traditional dorms & private rooms, along with a large open plan kitchen/dining/communal area make a great space to relax . Drying room and cycle storage available. Either book the whole hostel, a room or just a bed with no minimum stay. Excellent facilities, comfortable beds and a warm and friendly welcome awaits you - the kettle is always on!

DETAILS

- **Open** - All year. Reception 8-10am / 5-10pm. No daytime access.
- **Beds** - 29:1x8,1x6,1x4,1x2,3x3 (family)
- **Price/night** - Dorm beds from £18.70. Private rooms from £29.33.

CONTACT: Dominique or Daniel
Tel: 01339 753752
info@ballater-hostel.com
www.ballater-hostel.com
Ballater Hostel, Bridge Square, Ballater, AB35 5QJ

SMUGGLERS
HOSTEL

330

Welcome to the highest hostel in the Scottish Highlands. Located in the picturesque village of Tomintoul on the Cairgorm circular MTB route. This 4star 24 bed hostel is a mecca for mountainbikers roadbikers and walkers. There is free WiFi, a fully equipped self catering kitchen & dining area, dorms and ensuite private/family rooms and a small walled campsite. Drying room, bike wash & storage. All bedding provided.

DETAILS

- **Open** - March-October. All year for sole use. Reception 9-11am and 4-7pm.
- **Beds** - 24: 2 x 2/5 (family rooms), 1x6, 1x7, 1x4 (dorm rooms)
- **Price/night** - From £20. Private/family rooms from £70. Sole use from £350.

CONTACT: Kenny
Tel: 01807 580364, 07557 642727, 07787436837.
info@thesmugglershostel.co.uk
www.thesmugglershostel.co.uk
Main Street, Tomintoul, AB37 9EX

BRAEMAR LODGE
BUNKHOUSE
331a

ARDENBEG
BUNKHOUSE
331b

Surrounded by the beauty and tranquillity of Deeside, Braemar Lodge Hotel and Bunkhouse are just a two minute walk from the village. Braemar Lodge Hotel, a former Victorian shooting lodge, is set in extensive grounds. The great value bunkhouse provides comfortable accommodation for up to 12 people within the hotel grounds. The bunkhouse is equipped with two shower rooms, one of which is suitable for wheelchairs. There's a generous, fully equipped, self-catering kitchen, but you are welcome to sample the excellent hotel meals. All bed linen and towels are supplied.

Part of the award-winning Craggan Outdoors activity centre, Ardenbeg offers good value, well appointed bunkhouse accommodation with the extra benefit of a large private garden with BBQ, picnic tables & a children's play area. The property is situated on a quiet residential street in Grantown-on-Spey, the historic capital of Strathspey, just a 15 mins' drive from Aviemore and all its amenities. For adventures even closer at hand you can organise a whole host of activities through Craggan Outdoors.

DETAILS
- **Open** - All year. All day.
- **Beds** - 12: 3x4
- **Price/night** - From £17 per person

DETAILS
- **Open** - All year. 24 hours access.
- **Beds** - 23: 1x4, 1x5, 1x6, 1x8.
- **Price/night** - £19.20 - £26pp, subject to number of people & duration of stay.

CONTACT: Reception
Tel: 01339 741627
mail@braemarlodge.co.uk
www.braemarlodge.co.uk
6 Glenshee Rd, Braemar, AB35 5YQ

CONTACT: Keith & Jill Ballam
Tel: 01479 873283 / 01479 872824
info@cragganoutdoors.co.uk
cragganoutdoors.co.uk
Grant Road, Grantown-on-Spey, Moray
PH26 3LD

FINDHORN
VILLAGE HOSTEL
332

Findhorn Village Hostel is just a stone's throw from the beautiful Moray Coast. Great wildlife sites and the Speyside distilleries are within reach. The hostel provides newly renovated self-catering accommodation for groups or individuals. There are shared bunkrooms, a two person room and an en suite family room. A new annex (6 beds) has a small kitchenette and en suite shower rooms.

DETAILS

■ **Open** - All year. Office hours 10am-3pm Mon to Fri.

■ **Beds** - 31: 2x10, 1x3, 1x2/3 plus studio flat

■ **Price/night** - £20pp, groups of 10+ £18pp. Mates Cabin £40, Captains Suite £80, Lobster Pot £110.

CONTACT: Richard
Tel: 01309 692339 or 07496 230266
findhornvillagecentre@gmail.com
www.findhornvillagehostel.com
Church Place, Findhorn, Forres, Moray, IV36 3YR

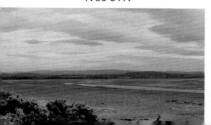

THE SAIL LOFT
BUNKHOUSE
333a

CRAIBSTONE
ESTATE
333b

Situated on the shore of the Moray Firth coast in Portsoy, The Sail Loft has a stunning location. Converted from a former sail making loft, The Sail Loft is modern and well equipped. It provides self-catering accommodation for 25 in a mixture of single accessible, twin, triple and bunk rooms, with secure cycle storage, cycle wash-down facilities and an outdoor wood fired hot tub. The Sail Loft is a short easy walk from Portsoy town centre and its charming 17th century historic harbour. Groups welcome.

Hostel accommodation - 5 minutes from Aberdeen Airport and 5 miles north from Aberdeen city centre. The accommodation is well placed for touring much of the North East of Scotland.

Easy access to the 'Granite City' with its striking granite architecture and rich and inspiring history. Families enjoy Codonas Amusement Park located at Aberdeen beach. Visit the dolphins that skirt the fringes of the busy harbour.

DETAILS

- **Open** - All year.
- **Beds** - 25: 1x6, 1x4, 2x3 (sgl), 4x2 (sgl), 1x1 (accessible)
- **Price/night** - From £25 per person.

CONTACT: Ian Tillett
Tel: 01261 842695 or 01261 842222
contact@portsoysailloft.org
www.portsoysailloft.org
Back Green, Portsoy, AB45 2AF

DETAILS

- **Open** - 22/06/20 to 14/08/20
- **Beds** - 103 beds in 95 rooms.
- **Price/night** - Standard room £15, en-suite room £20, twin en-suite £35.

CONTACT: Gwen Bruce
Tel: 01224 711012
accommodation@sruc.ac.uk
www.sruc.ac.uk/holidayletsaberdeen
Accommodation Office, Scotland's Rural College, Ferguson Building, Craibstone Estate, Bucksburn, Aberdeen, AB21 9YA

INVERNESS
STUDENT HOTEL

The cosy and friendly Student Hotel enjoys panoramic views of the town and the mountains beyond. Your perfect place to unwind, just yards from the city's varied night-life and a few mins' walk from bus and train stations. Relax in the fabulous lounge with real log fire and drink as much free tea, coffee & hot chocolate as you like. Visit the beautiful ancient pine forest of Glen Affric or the Culloden Battlefield. Famous Loch Ness lies just a few miles upstream and of course has its own special wild animal.

DETAILS

- **Open** - All year. All day. Reception 7am - 10.30pm.
- **Beds** - 57
- **Price/night** - From £18 per night. ID required for check in.

CONTACT: Receptionist
Tel: 01463 236556
info@invernessstudenthotel.com
www.invernessstudenthotel.com
8 Culduthel Road, Inverness, IV2 4AB

THE LOCHSIDE
HOSTEL

Perched right on the banks of Loch Ness, the Lochside Hostel has fantastic views up and down the loch and can give you direct access to the water's edge. Why not go for a dip in Scotland's largest water body? Take a walk to watch for wildlife? Or even hunt the elusive Nessie?

The Great Glen walking route passes the front door, and the End to End cycle route is nearby. Drumnadrochit is just 12 miles away by boat.

DETAILS

■ **Open** - April-October. Check in 18:00-23:00. Check out 10:30.
■ **Beds** - 47: 3x2 (twin), 2x4 (female), 5x4, 1x5, 1x8 all mixed dorms.
■ **Price/night** - From £15

CONTACT: Reception
Tel: 01320 351274
lochside@macbackpackerstours.com
lochsidehostel.com
Alltsigh, Inverness. IV63 7YD

LOCH NESS
BACKPACKERS LODGE
336a

SADDLE MOUNTAIN
HOSTEL
336b

This 18th-century Highland farmhouse provides warm & friendly hostel accommodation. Ideally situated within walking distance of Loch Ness, Urquhart Castle, on the Great Glen Way and with pubs, restaurants and supermarket close by. Residents-only bar offers over 50 Scottish beers and 25 Scotch whiskies. Hiking tours, fishing, watersports and mountain biking can all be arranged locally. Free parking. Pet-friendly (some rooms only - please contact us). Bike storage available except in Jul/Aug.

Saddle Mountain Hostel is a friendly 4* hostel in Invergarry, between Loch Ness & Fort William by the road to Skye.

Shortlisted for Hostel of the Year in The Great Outdoors Magazine Awards 2019, the hostel sleeps 22 in 5 rooms. It has a large kitchen, dining room & lounge, free WiFi, drying room & bike storage. Perfect for Munro bagging, long distance hiking, cycling, paddling & day trips.

DETAILS

- **Open** - All year except Feb. All day.
- **Beds** - 45: 2x7,3x6,1xtwin,1xdbl,2xfam.
- **Price/night** - From £17pp. Discounts apply to groups or long term stays

CONTACT: Patrick & Nikki Kipfmiller
Tel: 01456 450807
info@lochness-backpackers.com
www.lochness-backpackers.com
Coiltie Farmhouse, East Lewiston,
Drumnadrochit, Inverness, IV63 6UJ

DETAILS

- **Open** - Seasonal. Check website for availability. Check-in 4.30-10pm.
- **Beds** - 22: 1x6, 1x5 (dbl, 3 singles), 2x4, 1x3 (1 dbl, 1 single).
- **Price/night** - Dorms from £22pp. Private rooms from £18pp. Whole hostel prices on request.

CONTACT: Helen or Gregor
Tel: 01809 501412
info@saddlemountainhostel.scot
www.saddlemountainhostel.scot
Mandally Road, Invergarry, PH35 4HP

MORAGS LODGE
LOCH NESS

A multi-award winning 4* hostel with a range of rooms to meet all needs and budgets in the bustling village of Fort Augustus on the banks of Loch Ness. Your perfect base to explore the Loch Ness area and an ideal stop off on the Great Glen Way. Surrounded by stunning mountain scenery and set in wooded grounds the hostel boasts 24 hour self-catering facilities, excellent home-made cheap meal options, a rustic bar, free WiFi, bike hire and ample car parking.

DETAILS
- **Open** - All year. Check in from 4pm (earlier by arrangement).
- **Beds** - 75: 1x7, 6x6, 6x4, 4x2/3
- **Price/night** - From £25pp in dorm beds. Doubles/twins from £32pp. Family rooms from £84

CONTACT: Claire
Tel: 01320 366289
info@moragslodge.com
www.moragslodge.com
Bunoich Brae, Fort Augustus, PH32 4DG

GREAT GLEN
HOSTEL
338a

CALLANDER
HOSTEL
338b

Located between mountains and lochs 20 miles north of Fort William and 10 miles south of Loch Ness, the Great Glen Hostel is your ideal base. Perfect for touring the Highlands, bagging Munros or paddling rivers and lochs. It's only a short walk to the Great Glen Way. The hostel provides comfortable, well appointed accommodation in twin, family and dormitory rooms and has a shop where you can buy your essentials.

Situated in the town of Callander at the start of the Loch Lomond and Trossachs National Park, Callander Hostel is a great location for tourists and outdoor enthusiasts alike. With outstanding views over Ben Ledi this Visit Scotland 5* Hostel has comfortable beds, en suite rooms and a fully equipped self-catering kitchen. Everything you need for the perfect retreat. On the Rob Roy Way, Heart200 and NCR 7.

DETAILS

■ **Open** - All year. All day. Please call first Nov-March.
■ **Beds** 49: 3x2, 1x3, 4x5, 2x6, 1x8
■ **Price/night** - Dorm beds from £22. Twin rooms from £26 pp. Whole hostel for sole use from £500 per night.

CONTACT: The Manager
Tel: 01809 501430
bookings@greatglenhostel.com
www.greatglenhostel.com
South Laggan, Spean Bridge,
Invernesshire, PH34 4EA

DETAILS

■ **Open** - All year. 24 hr access. Check in 2-8pm
■ **Beds** - 30: 2x8, 1x6, 2x twin/double, 1 x family(4). All en suite
■ **Price/night** - From £18.50 per person in dorm, from £60 per twin/double en suite room.

CONTACT: Patricia
Tel: 01877 330141
bookings@callanderhostel.co.uk
www.callanderhostel.co.uk
6 Bridgend, Callander, FK17 8AH

ÀITE
CRUINNICHIDH

Àite Cruinnichidh, 15 miles northeast of Fort William, occupies a unique sheltered spot adjacent to the Monessie Gorge where you can explore remote glens, mountain passes and lochs. The hostel has a fully equipped kitchen/dining room, sitting room, excellent showers, sauna, seminar room and garden. All bedding is provided. Guests enjoy socialising and enjoy the natural environment that the hostel has to offer.

  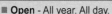

DETAILS

- **Open** - All year. All day.
- **Beds** - 28: 1x6, 4x4, 1x twin, 1x double, 1x family/double en suite.
- **Price/night** - From £18pp in dorms. Private rooms: dbl en suite £54, dbl/twin £44, small twin £42.

CONTACT: Gavin or Nicola
Tel: 01397 712315
gavin@highland-hostel.co.uk
www.highland-hostel.co.uk
1 Achluachrach, By Roy Bridge, Near Fort William, PH31 4AW

SMIDDY
BUNKHOUSE

Enjoy our loch-side location overlooking the Caledonian Canal, with Ben Nevis & Fort William 4 miles away. Ideal for the outdoor enthusiast with advice & guiding available for walking/climbing, river, loch and sea kayaking, open canoeing & dinghy sailing. Outdoor equipment hire available. After a busy day in the fresh air return to a welcome drying room & laundry, hot showers and a comfy private bunkroom ideal for families & groups.

DETAILS

- **Open** - All year. Check-in from 3pm – 8pm. Check-out 10am
- **Beds** - 24: 2x4,1x4 family,1x6,1x6 fam.
- **Price/night** - 4 bed room £92-£107; 4 bed ensuite £101-£119. 6 bed room £137-£160; 6 bed ensuite £147-£168.

CONTACT: John or Tina
Tel: 01397 772467
enquiry@highland-mountain-guides.co.uk
www.accommodation-fortwilliam.co.uk
Snowgoose Mountain Centre, Station Road, Corpach, Fort William, PH33 7JH

BANK STREET
LODGE

Bank Street Lodge is 100 metres from Fort William High Street with its shops, pubs & restaurants. There is a fully equipped kitchen with cooker, fridge, microwave, cutlery and crockery. The common room lounge has a TV, it also provides tables and chairs for meals and a snack vending machine. All bedding is provided. Some rooms are en-suite (twins, doubles and family). The en-suite rooms have recently been refurbished. WiFi is also available. 3 Star STB rating.

DETAILS

■ **Open** - All year except Xmas. All day access. Entry from 1pm, depart by 10am.
■ **Beds** - 43: 6x4, 4x3, 1x7. Various single, twin and family (4) ensuite rooms.
■ **Price/night** - From £18 to £25 per person. Group rates available.

CONTACT: Reception
Tel: 01397 700070
bankstreetlodge@btconnect.com
www.bankstreetlodge.co.uk
Bank Street, Fort William, PH33 6AY

FORT WILLIAM
BACKPACKERS

342

Surrounded by spectacular mountain scenery, Fort William is a mecca for those with a spirit of adventure. You can start (or end) the West Highland Way in Fort William, hike or bike along mountain trails, go for a boat trip on the sea loch or just take it easy amidst the wonderful scenery. Even in winter Fort William stays busy with skiing, snow-boarding, mountaineering and ice-climbing. Set on a hillside above the town, with wonderful views, this cosy hostel provides all you'll need after a day in the hills.

DETAILS

- **Open** - All year. All day. Reception 7am-noon & 5pm-10.30pm
- **Beds** - 38
- **Price/night** - From £18 per person. ID required for check-in.

CONTACT: Receptionist
Tel: 01397 700711
info@fortwilliambackpackers.com
www.fortwilliambackpackers.com
Alma Road, Fort William, PH33 6HB

CORRAN
HOUSE

343

A warm welcome & great value accommodation in Oban for singles, couples, families & groups. Enjoy a large self-catering kitchen, spacious lounge, comfortable rooms & big beds. Corran House is perfect for exploring Argyll & the inner Hebrides & is close to the bus, train & ferry. Downstairs try Markie Dans bar for tasty meals, live music & Highland hospitality.

DETAILS

■ **Open** - All year. Reception & check In: 3-10pm only.
■ **Beds** - 26 bunks: 5x4, 1x6. Plus 26 private guest rooms
■ **Price/night** - Bunks £18/£20 en suite. Guest rooms £27.50-£40pp (2 sharing). Singles from £45. Winter discounts.

CONTACT:
Tel: 01631 566040
enquiries@corranhouseoban.co.uk
www.corranhouseoban.co.uk
1-3 Victoria Cres, Corran Esplanade,
Oban, Argyll, PA34 5PN

OBAN
BACKPACKERS
344

Perfectly situated in the heart of Oban, the gateway to the Isles, just 10 mins' walk from the bus, train & ferry terminals, this friendly hostel is a great place to stay and unwind. The fabulous sociable lounge has a real fire, pool table, free WiFi, comfy sofas and unlimited free hot drinks. The kitchen is fully equipped, perfect for cooking your favourite meals. Large dorm beds come complete with bedding including 2 comfy pillows. The hot powerful showers are legendary! Knowledgeable and friendly staff will help you make the most of your time in Oban.

DETAILS

- **Open** - March - Nov. 7am - 10pm.
- **Beds** - 54: 1x12, 1x10, 1x8, 4x6
- **Price/night** - From £18. Whole hostel bookings please email for quote.

CONTACT: Reception
Tel: 01631 562107
info@obanbackpackers.com
www.obanbackpackers.com
Breadalbane Street, Oban, PA34 5NZ

BACKPACKERS
PLUS OBAN
345a

LISMORE
BUNKHOUSE
345b

Many people's favourite hostel thanks to its friendly atmosphere, the beautiful seaside town setting and its excellent facilities. Enjoy free WiFi, free breakfast, free all-day hot drinks, clean spacious rooms, secure bike storage, laundry service, communal areas, strong hot showers, comfortable rooms and a well-equipped self-catering kitchen. The lively town of Oban has direct ferry access to the many beautiful Scottish Isles.

This super warm and comfy eco bunkhouse on a traditional croft is the perfect base to explore the magical Isle of Lismore. The bunkhouse sleeps 12 in a mix of en suite dorms and private rooms and there is a campsite with 5 pitches and hook ups for 2 camper vans.
The Isle of Lismore is just 7 miles by car ferry from Oban and is a tranquil, unspoilt island surrounded by stunning mountain scenery. Perfect for wildlife and history as well as walkers, cyclists and those wanting to get away from it all. Home grown organic veg and bike hire.

DETAILS
- **Open** - All year. Reception 8am to 10:30am and 4pm to 10pm.
- **Beds** - 50-60 dorm beds, family, double, twin rooms, some en suite.
- **Price/night** - Dorms FROM £18.50pp. Private rooms FROM £23pp.

DETAILS
- **Open** - All year.
- **Beds** - 12
- **Price/night** - From £20pp. Exclusive hire available. Camping £10 pp.

CONTACT: Receptionist
Tel: 01631 567189
info@backpackersplus.com
www.backpackersplus.com
The Old Church, Breadalbane St,
Oban, Argyll, PA34 5PH

CONTACT: Clare
Tel: 07720 975433
lismorebunkhouse@gmail.com
www.fb.com/thelismorebunkhouse
Isle of Lismore, PA34 5UG

CRAIGNURE
BUNKHOUSE
346a

ROSS OF MULL
346b
BUNKROOMS

Craignure, a superior eco-sensitive bunkhouse, purpose built in 2014, is the perfect base for your Mull adventure. Set on the water's edge close to the ferry port, there's the Craignure Inn next door for traditional island hospitality. The 4 well-appointed bunkrooms have en suite showers and there's a spacious well appointed communal area with kitchen, ample dining and relaxing space.

Ross of Mull Bunkrooms are located less than a mile from the ferry link to Iona at Fionnphort. Ideal for exploring the superb wildlife, rich history & shell-sand beaches of the Ross of Mull, so loved by outdoor enthusiasts. Perfect for day trips to Staffa, the Treshnish Isles & Iona. There are two 4 bunk rooms, a well-equipped kitchen, woodburner & stunning views. For larger groups you can book a combined stay with Achaban House next door, which sleeps 14.

DETAILS

- **Open** - All year. Closed 11am-4pm for cleaning.
- **Beds** - 20: 2x4, 2x6
- **Price/night** - £24pp. 4 berth rms £90, 6 berth rms £135. Whole hostel £420 by prior arrangement. Weekend rates apply April-Oct. Discounts for multiple nights.

DETAILS

- **Open** - March - October. November - February whole bunkhouse only
- **Beds** - 8: 2x4
- **Price/night** - Per room: £99 (4 people), £86 (3 people), £73 (2 people). Sole use from £143.

CONTACT: Chris, Claire or Ivan
Tel: 01680 812043 or 07900 692973
info@craignure-bunkhouse.co.uk
www.craignure-bunkhouse.co.uk
Craignure Bunkhouse, Craignure, Isle Of Mull, Argyll And Bute, PA65 6AY

CONTACT: Rachel Ball
Tel: 07759 615200
info@rossofmullbunkrooms.co.uk
www.rossofmullbunkrooms.co.uk
Fionnphort, Isle of Mull PA66 6BL

IONA HOSTEL

347a

COLONSAY
BACKPACKERS LODGE

347b

Tucked into the rocky outcrops on a working croft, Iona Eco Hostel has spectacular views of the isles and mountains beyond. The land has been worked for generations, creating the familiar Hebridean patchwork of wildflower meadow, crops and grazing land. It offers quiet sanctuary for those that seek it, within easy reach of island activities. Whether travelling on your own, with friends, or as a group, Iona Hostel promises a warm welcome. Tourist board 4 star. Green Tourism Gold.

Come to Colonsay Backpackers Lodge and savour the idyll of this Inner Hebridean island. Explore the magnificent sandy beaches, ancient forests and beautiful lochs. Wildlife abounds; spot dolphins, seals, otters and many rare birds. The pub, café & shop are 3 miles away. Or buy fresh lobster, crab and oysters from the fishing boats. The lodge is a refurbished former gamekeeper's house with bothies. Centrally heated, it has 2 twin, 3 twin bunk and 2 three-bedded rooms. Free WiFi.

DETAILS

- **Open** - All year. Closed 11am-1pm for cleaning - no curfew.
- **Beds** - 21: 1x2, 2x4, 1x5, 1x6.
- **Price/night** - £23.00 adult / £19.00 under 10's (bedding included).

CONTACT: John MacLean
Tel: 01681 700781
info@ionahostel.co.uk
www.ionahostel.co.uk
Iona Hostel, Iona, Argyll, PA76 6SW

DETAILS

- **Open** - March to October. 24 hours
- **Beds** - 16: 5x2, 2x3
- **Price/night** - £28pp twin, £22pp bothy

CONTACT: The Manager
Tel: 01951 200211
cottages@colonsayholidays.co.uk
www.colonsayholidays.co.uk
Colonsay Estate Cottages, Isle of Colonsay, Argyll, PA61 7YP

ISLE OF MUCK
BUNKHOUSE
348

This self-catering hostel can also be hired as a holiday cottage. The bunkhouse overlooks the ferry port of Port Mor, it is near to The Craft Shop & Tearoom and to the island's Community Hall. The Isle of Muck is just 2 miles long by 1 mile wide and has a population of 46 people. With a rich cultural heritage and amazing wildlife, Muck is the perfect place to unwind. BYO towel and food supplies (no general store on Muck).

DETAILS

■ **Open** - All year. Monthly lets available out of season.
■ **Beds** - 8: 3x2(bunks) 1x2 (double)
■ **Price/night** - £22pp (plus £5 per stay for bed linen and £5 for towels). £90 sole use. £500 for a weeks sole use.

CONTACT: Georgia Gillies
Tel: 07833 195654
bunkhouse@isleofmuck.com
www.isleofmuck.com
Isle of Muck, Port Mor, Isle of Muck,
PH41 2RP

GLEBE BARN

Glebe Barn offers 4* homely accommodation on the extraordinary Isle of Eigg within 1 mile of the island shop & café/restaurant. Outstanding sea views and sleeping up to 22 in twin, triple, family & dorm rooms. Perfect for individuals, families or groups. Also two person mezzanine apartment.

DETAILS

■ **Open** - Groups all year; individuals from April to October. Open 24 hours.
■ **Beds** - 22: 1x2, 2x3, 1x6, 1x8.
■ **Price/night** - Dormitory bed: £21 (1-2 nights), £19 (3+ nights), £17 (6+ nights). Twin room £47 (1-2 nights), £43 (3+ nights), £39 (6+nights). Triple room £63 (1-2 nights), £57 (3+ nights), £52 (6+ nights). Contact for quote for groups.

CONTACT: Tamsin or Stuart
Tel: 01687 315099
mccarthy@glebebarn.co.uk
www.glebebarn.co.uk
Glebe Barn, Isle of Eigg, Inner Hebrides, PH42 4RL

COLL
BUNKHOUSE
350a

MILLHOUSE
HOSTEL
350b

Coll Bunkhouse 5* self-catering hostel accommodation is a mile from the ferry terminal & close to local amenities. Ideal for groups or individuals, short or longer stays. A half hour from the mainland by plane, under 3 hours by ferry. This beautiful Hebridean island is ideal for walking, stargazing, wildlife, cycling, water sports or chilling amidst stunning scenery. Visit quiet and beautiful spaces and beaches and enjoy fine island hospitality. A warm welcome awaits you.

Tiree is an idyllic Hebridean island surrounded by white beaches and crystal clear seas. Perfect for outdoor pursuits & wildlife enthusiasts, Millhouse offers you 4* facilities and free WiFi. You can hire bikes, visit the lighthouse museum, watch the seals or enjoy watersports at Loch Bhasapol (200m away). For walkers Tiree Pilgrimage route passes close by. Tiree has a resident RSPB warden and there are handy bird and otter hides for you to use.

DETAILS

- **Open** - All year. 24 hours.
- **Beds** - 16: 2x6, 1x4
- **Price/night** - £22pp (dorm). Private rooms from £110 (quin), £80 (quad), £65 (triple), £50 (twin). Discount of 10% to 55% for sole use for 2 nights or more.

CONTACT: Jane
Tel: 01879 230217
info@collbunkhouse.co.uk
www.collbunkhouse.com
Arinagour, Isle of Coll, Argyll, PA78 6SY

DETAILS

- **Open** - Mar-Oct. (Winter by arrangement). Open all day. Check in 4pm. Check out 10am.
- **Beds** - Hostel 16 : 2 x 2/3, 2 x 5.
- **Price/night** - Dorm from £25pp. Private room from £43pp.

CONTACT: Kris Milne
Tel: 01879 220802 or 07786 708154
mail@tireemillhouse.co.uk
www.tireemillhouse.co.uk
Cornaigmore, Isle of Tiree, PA77 6XA

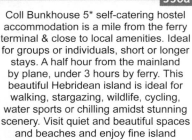

GLENFINNAN
SLEEPING CAR
351a

ARDNAMURCHAN
BUNKHOUSE
351b

Glenfinnan Sleeping Car provides unique accommodation in an historic railway carriage next to Glenfinnan Station & close to Glenfinnan Viaduct (featured in Harry Potter films). An ideal location for the mountains, a good starting point for bothy expeditions & a useful stop-over en route to Skye. Fully equipped kitchen, shower & drying room. The dining coach provides excellent meals in the daytime & evening meals are available close by.

Ardnamurchan Bunkhouse is in Glenborrodale on the Ardnamurchan Peninsula, one of the UK's last unspoiled coastal wildernesses.

This recently renovated eco-bunkhouse sleeping 16 people in eight bedrooms, with a well-equipped kitchen, flexible dining tables, free Wi-Fi and parking.

DETAILS
- **Open** - All year (enquire for winter opening details).
- **Beds** - 10
- **Price/night** - £35 per twin bunk compartment per night (£25 single occ.) £5 bedding/towel hire. £150 sole use.

CONTACT: Amy
Tel: 01397 722295
glenfinnanstationmuseum@gmail.com
www.glenfinnanstationmuseum.co.uk
Glenfinnan Station, Glenfinnan, nr Fort William, PH37 4LT

DETAILS
- **Open** - March to October
- **Beds** - 16: 2x1, 3x2, 2 doubles and 1xfamily (dbl +bunks)
- **Price/night** - From: Twin room £50. Double room £58. Family room £78. Single room £38. Contact for prices for groups and sole use throughout the year.

CONTACT: Fay and Niall Rowantree
Tel: 01972 500 742 or 07749 727 878
admin@theardnamurchanbunkhouse.co.uk
www.theardnamurchanbunkhouse.co.uk
Glenborrodale, Ardnamurchan, West Highlands, Scotland PH36 4JP

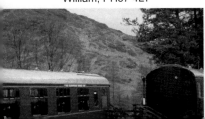

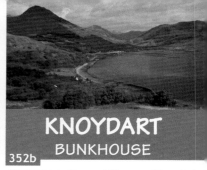

SHEENAS
BACKPACKERS LODGE
352a

352b
KNOYDART
BUNKHOUSE

The Backpackers Lodge, the oldest croft house in Mallaig, offers a homely base from which to explore the Inner Hebrides, the famous white sands of Morar and the remote peninsula of Knoydart. Mallaig is a working fishing village with all the excitement of the boats landing. You can see the seals playing in the harbour and take whale and dolphin watching trips. The hostel provides excellent budget accommodation with central heating, a well equipped kitchen/common room and free WiFi. Hot water and heating provided by renewable energy.

Welcome to the world famous Knoydart Foundation Bunkhouse on the stunning remote peninsula of Knoydart on the west coast of Scotland reachable only by boat or a long hike. Community run, the Bunkhouse uses hydro electricity & promotes responsible tourism. Set amid wild, remote terrain overlooking a mesmerising beach. Ten mins' walk to pub, PO, shop & ferry at Inverie. 3 bedrooms & comfy communal areas. Ranger service & deer stalking available. Stunning dark skies, so bring a torch!

DETAILS
- **Open** - All year. 9am-8pm
- **Beds** - 12: 2 x 6
- **Price/night** - £24 per person.

DETAILS
- **Open** - All year.
- **Beds** - 26: 1x7, 1x8, 1x11
- **Price/night** - £20 adult, £12 under 16s. Block bookings £440. Dogs £5/night.

CONTACT: Ashley or Fraser
Tel: 01687 462764
backpackers@btinternet.com
www.mallaigbackpackers.co.uk
Harbour View, Mallaig, Inverness-shire,
PH41 4PU

CONTACT: Fiona
Tel: 01687 462163
bunkhouse@knoydart.org
www.knoydart-foundation.com
Inverie, Knoydart, By Mallaig, Inverness-shire PH41 4PL

KNOYDART
LODGE

Knoydart Lodge, on the magical and remote Knoydart Peninsula, is accessible only by ferry. The Lodge offers high quality accommodation at bunkhouse prices. Luxury abounds, from the fresh linens & fluffy towels in each of the five en-suite bedrooms to the spacious communal areas with high vaulted ceilings, open beam architecture and gorgeous views. Continental breakfast comes as standard & pick up from the ferry can be provided.

DETAILS

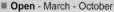

- **Open** - March - October
- **Beds** - 20: 1x6, 3x4, 1x2 (all en suite)
- **Price/night** - £40pp for a private room with continental breakfast (min 2 people). Children £20pp.

CONTACT: Stephanie Harris
Tel: 01687 460129
stay@knoydartlodge.co.uk
www.knoydartlodge.co.uk
Market Garden, Inverie, Knoydart, By Mallaig, Inverness-shire PH41 4PL

SKYE
BACKPACKERS
354

Whether your visit to Skye is to tackle the mighty mountains, meet the legendary faeries or simply to chill out, Skye Backpackers is the place for you. Located in the fishing village of Kyleakin surrounded by mountains and sea, the hostel has dorm, double and twin rooms. All beds come with sheets, duvets and 2 pillows. There is a fully equipped self-catering kitchen, a sunny dining area, as much free tea, coffee & hot chocolate as you can drink, free WiFi, a cosy lounge with a real fire and spectacular views.

DETAILS
- **Open** - All year. All day. Reception 7am-12am & 5pm-10pm (times may vary).
- **Beds** - 39
- **Price/night** - From £15pp. ID required for check in.

CONTACT: Receptionist
Tel: 01599 534510
info@skyebackpackers.com
www.skyebackpackers.com
Benmhor, Kyleakin, Skye, IV41 8PH

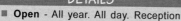

SKYE BASECAMP

355

Skye Basecamp is a fabulous centrally located hostel with individual beds in small dormitories & private en suite rooms. Perfect for lovers of the great outdoors, with hot showers, comfy beds and a great drying room. Shops & bars all within walking distance. Knowledgeable staff and enthusiastic guests create a fantastic atmosphere. Join us for sunset panoramas across the shores of Broadford Bay or take a stroll to the beach with its resident otters.

DETAILS

- **Open** - All year. All day. Check in 4-10pm.
- **Beds** - 36
- **Price/night** - Seasonal from £20pp. Discounts for groups/sole use.

CONTACT: Catriona & Mike Lates
Tel: 01471 820044
bookings@skyebasecamp.co.uk
www.skyebasecamp.co.uk
Lime Park, Broadford,
Isle of Skye IV49 9AE

WATERFRONT
BUNKHOUSE

Feet from the edge of Loch Harport, Isle of Skye, with breathtaking views of the Cuillins, this purpose built, stylish & comfortable bunkhouse is an ideal base for hill walkers or sightseers. There is spectacular scenery and abundant wildlife in the surrounding hills and glens. The bunkhouse has a kitchen and common room with a balcony overlooking the loch and 5 bunkrooms, one en suite. The Old Inn, a traditional highland pub provides breakfast, lunch and dinner if required.

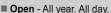

DETAILS

■ **Open** - All year. All day.
■ **Beds** - 24: 2x6, 2x4, 1x4 en suite.
■ **Price/night** - £25pp, en suite: £28pp. Sole use £550. Booking essential.

CONTACT: Elaine
Tel: 01478 640205
enquiries@theoldinnskye.co.uk
www.theoldinnskye.co.uk
The Old Inn, Carbost,
Isle of Skye, IV47 8SR

HEB
HOSTEL

357a

357b

LAXDALE
BUNKHOUSE

The Heb Hostel is a family-run backpackers hostel in the heart of Stornoway on the enchanting Isle of Lewis. It is an ideal stop/stay for travellers visiting the Hebrides. Cyclists, walkers, surfers, families and groups are all welcome. Clean, comfortable, friendly and relaxed, Heb Hostel aims to provide you with a quality stay at budget prices. There are many facilities, including a common room with peat fire, free WiFi, local guides and information.

Laxdale Bunkhouse, on the Isle of Lewis, lies within Laxdale Holiday Park, a small family-run park set in peaceful leafy surroundings. Just 1.5 miles away from the town of Stornoway, it's an ideal base for exploring the island. Built in 1998, the bunkhouse has four rooms of four bunks. There is a drying room, a spacious fully equipped dining kitchen, a comfortable TV lounge and BBQ area. Toilets/ showers are located in the building & are suitable for the disabled. Wigwams are also available.

DETAILS

- **Open** - March - October. Open all day but may need to phone for access code.
- **Beds** - 26: 1x8, 2x7,1x4 (family room).
- **Price/night** - Dorm £20pp Family room £80pn for family, £90pn for adults only.

CONTACT: Christine Macintosh
Tel: 01851 709889
christine@hebhostel.com
www.hebhostel.com
25 Kenneth St, Stornoway, Isle of Lewis, HS1 2DR

DETAILS

- **Open** - March to Nov. 9am - 10pm.
- **Beds** - 16: 4x4.
- **Price/night** - £19 adult, £17 child, £70 room (3 or less people) £265 sole use.

CONTACT: Gordon Macleod
Tel: 01851 706966 / 01851 703234
info@laxdaleholidaypark.com
www.laxdaleholidaypark.com
Laxdale Holiday Park, 6 Laxdale Lane, Stornoway, Isle of Lewis, HS2 0DR

GALSON FARM
HOSTEL
358a

GEARRANNAN
HOSTEL & BUNKHOUSE
358b

This fully equipped bunkhouse on the Isle of Lewis enjoys stunning views of the Atlantic coast towards the Butt of Lewis Lighthouse. It provides the perfect haven from which to explore the west side of Lewis, with sandy beaches, wildlife and historic sites on the doorstep. A short walk through the croft takes you to the shore and river, where there is an abundance of birds & otters are regular visitors. The hostel has one dormitory with 6 beds, two shower/toilet rooms and a kitchen/dining room. Bedding, bike shed & drying facilities are included.

Part of the Gearrannan Blackhouse Village on the Isle of Lewis, the Gearrannan Hostel has been refurbished to sleep 13 including a 3 bed family room. Warm and cosy it has a well equipped kitchen & two modern shower rooms. The bunkhouse (groups only) sleeps 14 in bunks. The perfect base for many local attractions from surfing to country walks, archaeology to cycling. There are also 3 holiday cottages.

DETAILS

- **Open** - All year.
- **Beds** - Hostel: 13: 1x10 1x3. Bunkhouse: 14: 2x6 1x2. Black houses: 1x2, 2x3-5
- **Price/night** - From £20 per person. Family room £65.

DETAILS

- **Open** - All year. All day.
- **Beds** - 6: 1x6
- **Price/night** - £22 pp. Sole use £125.

CONTACT: Elaine & Richard
Tel: 01851 850492 or 07970 219682
stay@galsonfarm.co.uk
www.galsonfarm.co.uk
Galson Farm House, South Galson, Isle of Lewis, HS2 0SH

CONTACT: Mairi
Tel: 01851 643416
info@gearrannan.com
www.gearrannan.com
5a Gearrannan Carloway Isle of Lewis HS2 9AL

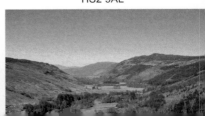

RAVENSPOINT
HOSTEL
359a

Nº5
DRINISHADER
359b

On the unspoilt Isle of Lewis, Ravenspoint Hostel sits on the shores of Loch Erisort, providing comfortable accommodation in a traditional crofting community where Gaelic is still spoken on a daily basis.

Whether travelling by bike, car or on foot, look out for white-tailed eagles, otters, deer and enjoy exploring the community-owned Pairc Estate on which the hostel sits alongside a small shop, tea-room, fuel service and museum.

Nº5 Drinishader is on the Isle of Harris, 5 miles from Tarbert & 8 miles from the famous white sandy beaches. Situated above Drinishader harbour, overlooking the beautiful East Loch Tarbert, the hostel & self-catering units provide a variety of accommodation for individuals, families & groups. Pick-up services from Tarbert can be arranged for a small cost. Your perfect base for coastal/hill walking, cycling, kayaking, boat trips, sightseeing and bird/wildlife watching. Breakfast & packed lunches can be provided.

DETAILS

- **Open** - Open from 1 Mar to 31 Oct.
- **Beds** - 9: 1xdbl, 1xtwin, 1x5. + 1 pitch.
- **Price/night** - Dorm £20 pp, Private Twin/Double £47.Inc bedding & hot drinks.

CONTACT: Ishbel
Tel: 01851 880236
hostel@ravenspoint.net
ravenspoint.net
Kershader, South Lochs, Isle of Lewis, HS2 9QA

DETAILS

- **Open** - May shut for some of the winter months. Reception 7am-10pm
- **Beds** - 10
- **Price/night** - From £21pp. Reductions for families, groups and longer stays.

CONTACT: Alyson
Tel: 01859 511255 or 07833 474743
info@number5.biz
www.number5.biz
5 Drinishader, Isle of Harris, HS3 3DX

BACKPACKERS
STOP
360a

360b

SANACHAN
BUNKHOUSE

Situated in the village of Tarbert on the Isle of Harris, the Backpackers Stop is a comfortable hostel for travellers. Close to the ferry, bus, shops, cafés, bars and restaurants. The Backpackers Stop is a handy base for exploring Harris, as well as whilst walking or cycling the islands. Ideal when arriving by ferry.

Self-catering kitchen, lounge & shared dorms. Linen, duvets & towels provided. USB sockets, free WiFi. Tea & coffee available all day. Basic self service breakfast provided. Keycode entry.

Sanachan Bunkhouse, in Kishorn, is the perfect base for walking, climbing, kayaking, cycling & sailing in Wester Ross. After a fun-filled day, your group can return to a warm bunkhouse, comfy bunks, hot showers and simple living. There is parking for six cars and beds for twelve, split between three rooms (please bring a sleeping bag). The bunkhouse is well equipped for self-catering, with enough tables & chairs for everyone. Laundry/drying, outside recreation and BBQ.

DETAILS

- **Open** - 1st March - 10th November. All year round for large groups/private use.
- **Beds** - 22: 4 rooms
- **Price/night** - £25 per person.

DETAILS

- **Open** - All year.
- **Beds** - 12: 1x6, 1x4, 1x2
- **Price/night** - £17 pp. Discounted student rate of £15 pp.

CONTACT: Lee
Tel: 01859 502742 or 07708 746745
bpackers_stop@hotmail.com
www.backpackers-stop.co.uk
Main St., Tarbert, Isle of Harris, HS3 3DJ

CONTACT: Sean and Sophie
Tel: 01520 733484
bookings@ourscottishadventure.com
www.ourscottishadventure.com
Sanachan Bunkhouse, Kishorn,
Strathcarron, Ross-shire, IV54 8XA

GERRYS
HOSTEL
361a

KINLOCHEWE
BUNKHOUSE
361b

Gerry's Hostel is situated in an excellent mountaineering and wilderness area on the most scenic railway in Britain. It is on the Cape Wrath Trails, The T.G.O Challenge Route and is 0.5 miles from the Coulin Pass at Craig. It sleeps 20; 10 in a large dormitory with comfy beds, the rest in 5/6 bed family rooms. Meals and draught ale are a 15 min drive away. Your perfect base for many activities including walking, climbing, fishing, cycling, golfing and wildlife watching.

Walkers, climbers and mountain bikers enjoying the Torridon Mountains and wilderness areas will be warmly welcomed at the Kinlochewe Hotel and Bunkhouse. Situated on the North Coast 500 road route, within 20 miles of over 20 Munros, the bunkhouse boasts a well equipped, self-catering kitchen, an efficient drying room, hot showers, internet and a 12 bunk dormitory. The hotel bar serves excellent home-made food and is in the 2018 Good Beer Guide.

DETAILS
- **Open** - All year. Check in after 4pm
- **Beds** - 20: 1x10, 2x5 or 6
- **Price/night** - From £20pp main dorm. Family room from £20pp (min 3 guests). Twins and doubles £25pp.

DETAILS
- **Open** - All year. 8am - 10pm.
- **Beds** - 12
- **Price/night** - £20 pp with discounts for groups booking sole occupancy.

CONTACT: Simon Howkins
Tel: 07894 984294, 01520 766232
s.howkins@gmail.com
gerryshostel.com
Craig Achnashellach, Strathcarron, Wester Ross, IV54 8YU

CONTACT: Dave and Karen Twist
Tel: 01445 760253
info@kinlochewehotel.co.uk
www.kinlochewehotel.co.uk
Kinlochewe by Achnasheen, Wester Ross, IV22 2PA

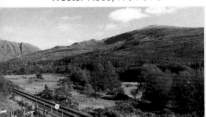

FOREST WAY
BUNKHOUSE
362a

THE CEILIDH PLACE
BUNKHOUSE
362b

Close to the idyllic fishing village of Ullapool in a peaceful rural setting with lots of wildlife.

A perfect base for climbers & walkers with 22 Munros and many other hills in the area. Next to Lael Forest Gardens which is renowned for its wildlife. The bunkhouse is ideally located for touring the North West Highlands with easy access to the areas of Torridon and up to Assynt.

The Ceilidh Place, in the centre of Ullapool, is a unique small complex, consisting of a music venue/performance space, restaurant, hotel, bar, bookshop, coffee shop, gallery and bunkhouse. There are regular ceilidhs, concerts & plays. The bunkhouse (group only) does not have self-catering facilities but the coffee shop is open from 8.30am to late evening all week including weekends. Rooms are also available in the hotel. The village of Ullapool is a small exciting port and fishing town, with ferries from the Outer Hebrides. Hill walkers and families especially love staying here.

DETAILS

- **Open** - All year.
- **Beds** - 8: 2x4 (en suite)
- **Price/night** - £20pp, £80 per room, £160 for the whole hostel. Discounts for stays of more than 1 night (see website for more info).

CONTACT: Iain
Tel: 01854 655330 or 07912 177419
bookings@forestway.co.uk
www.forestway.co.uk
Lael, Lochbroom, IV23 2RS

DETAILS

- **Open** - All year.
- **Beds** - Bunkhouse: 32,
- **Price/night** - Get in touch for prices.

CONTACT: Effie
Tel: 01854 612103
stay@theceilidhplace.com
www.theceilidhplace.com
14 West Argyle St. Ullapool, IV26 2TY

BADRALLACH
BOTHY & CAMPSITE

On the tranquil shores of Little Loch Broom overlooking one of Scotland's finest mountain ranges, Badrallach Bothy and Campsite offer a fine base for walking and climbing. Fish in the rivers, hill lochs and sea or simply enjoy the flora and fauna. Hot showers, spotless accommodation, an unbelievable price and total peace make the Bothy and Campsite a firm favourite. There is also a holiday cottage for hire.

DETAILS

- **Open** - All year. All day.
- **Beds** - 12: (area is for sleeping mats and bags - no beds)
- **Price/night** - £8pp, £2 per vehicle. £100 sole use. See @badrallachcampsite facebook page for camping/cottage fees.

CONTACT: Chris Davidson
Tel: 07435 123 190
mail@badrallach.com
www.badrallach.com
Croft No 9, Badrallach, Dundonnell,
Ross-shire, IV23 2QP

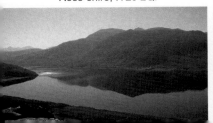

INCHNADAMPH
LODGE

Inchnadamph Lodge has been tastefully converted to provide quality hostel accommodation at a budget price. There's a large self-catering kitchen, lounge and dining room. The newly converted annex offer a choice of en suite rooms. At the foot of Ben More Assynt, overlooking Loch Assynt, stay and explore one of the wildest areas in the Highlands.

DETAILS
- **Open** - Mid March to Mid Oct. All day
- **Beds** - 60: Lodge: 4x2 (twin), 3 x family, 2x6, 2x8. Annex: 3 x family. Two shepherds hut 2x2.
- **Price/night** - £22-25pp (dormitory), £30-£40(twin)pp including continental breakfast and linen. Group discounts.

CONTACT: Chris
Tel: 01571 822218
info@inch-lodge.co.uk
www.inch-lodge.co.uk
Inchnadamph, Assynt, Nr Lochinver,
Sutherland, IV27 4HL

BLACK ROCK
BUNKHOUSE
365a

365b

BUNKHOUSE
@ INVERSHIN HOTEL

Situated in beautiful Glenglass and sheltered by Ben Wyvis, this comfortable bunkhouse is an ideal base for touring the Highlands. The bunkhouse is at the eastern end of a hikers' route across Scotland and on the Land's End to John O'Groats route. The village has a general shop, Post Office, bus service and an inn (serving good bar meals and breakfasts) 250m away. There is also a camping ground. All areas of the bunkhouse are easily accessible by wheelchair and suitable for the disabled.

Situated within a small hotel in the north Highlands, the bunkhouse consists of 4 rooms with a shared shower room & toilet. Guests can enjoy the hotel facilities; comfortable reception area, cosy bar with real fire, real ale and regular music sessions. Cyclists, walkers, bikers, fishermen, Munro baggers, families and individuals are all welcome. The bunkhouse is just off the North Coast 500 road route. No self-catering facilities but breakfast & evening meals are available.

DETAILS

- **Open** - April 1st to October 31st. 24hr access. New arrivals 12noon -7pm.
- **Beds** - 16 : 4 x 4.
- **Price/night** - £17 per person. 10% off for groups of 8

DETAILS

- **Open** - April-end Sept. Check in 4pm.
- **Beds** - 10: 2x twin, 2x triple (bunkbeds).
- **Price/night** - £20pp. Breakfast: £5 or £10. Discount for groups of 6 or more.

CONTACT: Lillian
Tel: 01349 830917
blackrockholidays@gmail.com
www.blackrockscotland.com
Evanton, Dingwall, Ross-shire, IV16 9UN

CONTACT: Angus or Cheryl
Tel: 01549 421202
enquiries@invershin.com
www.invershin.com
Invershin Hotel, Lairg, Sutherland,
IV27 4ET

HELMSDALE
HOSTEL

366a

Set in the scenic coastal village of Helmsdale, the hostel (which was completely refurbished in 2018) has en suite private rooms, a fully equipped kitchen and comfortable lounge area with log burning stove. On the NC500 and Land's End to John O'Groats route, the hostel is popular with 'end to enders' and walkers exploring the Marilyn Hills. A perfect stop on the way to Orkney. Dogs on request. Groups welcome.

DETAILS
- **Open** - All Year (Nov-Mar group bookings only).
- **Beds** - 24: 6x4 (en-suite)
- **Price/night** - Adults from £26. Children from £15. Dog £10. Ensuite from £70/room.

CONTACT: Marie
Tel: Marie 07971 922356 or Hostel Office 07927933721
stay@helmsdalehostel.co.uk
www.helmsdalehostel.co.uk
Stafford Street, Helmsdale, Sutherland, KW8 6JR

SANDRAS
HOSTEL

366b

Thurso is the northern-most town on the UK mainland. The cliffs are alive with guillemots, kittiwakes, fulmars & puffins, while the sea is home to seals & porpoises. The 4* hostel has en suites in all rooms, (some have TVs). Using their own backpacking experience, the owners ensure you will enjoy a level of comfort and service second to none. Surfing, pony trekking, fishing, quad biking, coastal walks and boat trips are all available nearby. On the NC500 route.

DETAILS
- **Open** - All year
- **Beds** - 26: 2x4 1x6 1x3 4x2
- **Price/night** - Dorm £20pp. Double/twin £46. Family room £75 (4 people), £90 (5 people). Breakfast is included in the price.

CONTACT: George or James
Tel: 01847 894575
info@sandras-backpackers.co.uk
www.sandras-backpackers.co.uk
24-26 Princes Street, Thurso, Caithness, KW14 7BQ

CORNMILL
BUNKHOUSE
367a

KYLE OF TONGUE
HOSTEL AND CAMPSITE
367b

Cornmill Bunkhouse is situated on a traditional croft. The mill was built in the early 1800s and was active until 1920s. It is now 4* accommodation for individuals or groups. Guests are reminded of their historic setting; the smaller bunkroom has a patio door looking onto the workings of the old mill with its large wooden cog driving wheels. Activities can be organised for groups including laser tagging & shooting. Hen and stag parties welcome.

The Kyle of Tongue Holiday Park is a stone lodge and campsite, magnificently situated on the shores of a sea loch on the Scottish North Coast. Furnished, like a boutique hotel, but with all the friendliness of a hostel. There are comfortable private bedrooms, roomy dormitories and relaxing communal areas. The campsite is well equipped and has panoramic views of Castle Varich, Ben Hope & Ben Loyal. Holiday cottage and static caravan also available.

DETAILS

- **Open** - All year, advanced notice required 1st Oct - 1st April. All day.
- **Beds** - 14: 1x8,1x6
- **Price/night** - £18 per person. Discounts available for group bookings.

DETAILS

- **Open** - All year. Check in from 4pm.
- **Beds** - 36 in hostel, plus cottage, static caravan and a large campsite.
- **Price/night** - From £21. Private rooms from £50. Contact for other prices.

CONTACT: Sandy Murray
Tel: 01641 571219   Mob: 07808 197350
sandy.murray2@btinternet.com
www.achumore.co.uk
Cornmill Bunkhouse, Achumore,
Strathhalladale, Sutherland, KW13 6YT

CONTACT: Richard Mackay
Tel: 01847 611789
kothostelandhp@btinternet.com
www.tonguehostelandholidaypark.co.uk
Kyle of Tongue Hostel & Holiday Park,
Tongue, By Lairg, Sutherland, IV27 4XH

ORCADES
HOSTEL

Orcades Hostel in Kirkwall, the capital of Orkney, is an excellent base for exploring the Isles. Accommodation is in doubles, twins, 4 & 6 bedded rooms. Each bedroom has en suite toilet/shower rooms. TVs and all bedding is provided. There is a stylish kitchen, a lounge with DVD & games and WiFi throughout the building.

A warm and friendly welcome awaits you at this comfortable 4 star hostel.

DETAILS

■ **Open** - All year. Check in after 2pm. Check out by 10am on day of departure.
■ **Beds** - 34: doubles, twin, 4 and 6 bed
■ **Price/night** - £22 pp in a shared room, £60 for a double or twin room. Winter rates available.

CONTACT: Erik or Sandra
Tel: 01856 873745
orcadeshostel@hotmail.co.uk
www.orcadeshostel.com
Muddisdale Road, Kirkwall, KW15 1RS

HOY
CENTRE
369a

HAMNAVOE
HOSTEL
369b

Surrounded by magnificent scenery, the Hoy Centre is ideally situated for a peaceful and relaxing holiday. It's also an ideal venue for outdoor education, weddings, workshops, clubs or family gatherings. Offering high quality, 4* accommodation, the centre has a well equipped kitchen, comfortable lounge & a large dining hall. All rooms are en suite with twin beds and one set of bunks. Hoy is an RSPB reserve comprising 3,500ha of upland heath and cliffs with a large variety of wildlife including arctic hares.

Accommodation on the waterfront at Stromness, Orkney, close to the ferry. Single, family and twin rooms with glorious views. Light, airy kitchen and a large dining table with views of the harbour. Lounge with comfortable seating, TV, DVDs and books. Laundry room, WiFi, free long stay car park. Visit the nearby islands of Graemsay and Hoy, check out the World Heritage sites. Relax in the tranquility of island life.

DETAILS

■ **Open** - All year.
■ **Beds** - 32
■ **Price/night** - Please phone for prices for singles, families or groups. Either on a daily or residential basis.

DETAILS

■ **Open** - All year. All day. No curfew. Check in after 2pm (reconfirm if not arriving before 7pm), check out by 10am.
■ **Beds** - 13: 1x4, 1x1, 4x2.
■ **Price/night** - From £21pp. Private rooms £23pp

CONTACT: Customer Services
Tel: 01856 873535 ext 2901
stromnesscs@orkney.gov.uk
www.orkney.gov.uk
Hoy, Orkney, KW16 3NJ

CONTACT: Mr George Argo
Tel: 01856 851202
info@hamnavoehostel.co.uk
www.hamnavoehostel.co.uk
10a North End Road, Stromness,
Orkney, KW16 3AG

BROWNS
HOSTEL & HOUSES

370

Providing nightly or weekly self-catering accommodation in the captivating small town of Stromness, Orkney. Within walking/cycling distance of the ancient Maeshowe, Ring of Brodgar and Skara Brae. Stromness has a museum, art centre, festival, scuba diving, free fishing and ferries from mainland Scotland. Facilities include well equipped kitchens, comfy sitting rooms and beds in single, double, twin, triple and family rooms, all with towels and bedding provided. Computers with internet and WiFi. Cycle storage & free car park up the lane.

DETAILS

- **Open** - All year. All day. No curfew.
- **Beds** - 28: 3x1,4x2,3x3,2x4
- **Price/night** - From £22 per person.

CONTACT: Sylvia Brown
Tel: 01856 850661
info@brownsorkney.co.uk
www.brownsorkney.co.uk
45/47 Victoria Street, Stromness,
Orkney, KW16 3BS

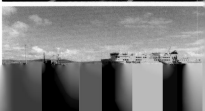

RACKWICK
HOSTEL
371a

BIRSAY
OUTDOOR CENTRE
371b

In the scenic Rackwick Valley in the north of Hoy, the 3* hostel overlooks Rackwick Bay considered one of the most beautiful places in Orkney. It sleeps 8 across 2 rooms of 4 beds. There's a small kitchen with a good range of utensils, and a separate dining area. Singles, families and groups are welcome for private room or whole hostel bookings. Car parking and bike storage behind the hostel. Walkers and Cyclist Welcome

Birsay Hostel in the northwest corner of the Orkney mainland offers comfortable accommodation for up to 26 in 5 bedrooms. An ideal venue for outdoor education trips, clubs or family gatherings. It has a well equipped kitchen, dining area, drying room, disabled access and all bed linen is provided. There is a campsite in the extensive grounds. Close to spectacular coast, RSPB reserves, early settlements and UNESCO heritage sites.

DETAILS

- **Open** - April - September
- **Beds** - 8: 2x4
- **Price/night** - For prices please check accommodation's website or phone.

CONTACT: Customer Services
Tel: 01856 850907 or 01856 873535 ext 2901
stromnesscs@orkney.gov.uk
www.orkney.gov.uk
Rackwick Hostel, Rackwick, Hoy, Orkney, KW16 3NJ

DETAILS

- **Open** - April - Sept. Groups all year.
- **Beds** - 26: 2x4,1x2,1x6,1x10 + camping.
- **Price/night** - Prices on enquiry. Private rooms or whole hostel bookings.

CONTACT: Customer Services
Tel: 01856 850907 or 01856 873535 ext 2901
stromnesscs@orkney.gov.uk
www.orkney.gov.uk
Birsay, Orkney, KW17 2LY

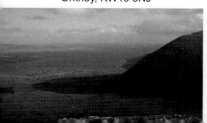

AYRES ROCK
HOSTEL

Sanday is the perfect place to take time out, with long stretches of unspoilt sandy beaches, an abundance of birds, seals and other wildlife, glittering seas, clear air and spectacular skies. Those lucky enough to live here enjoy a rare quality of life in a small, friendly and safe community. Enjoy the views over the Holms of Ire from the conservatory in this 4* hostel.

DETAILS

- **Open** - All year. 8am to 10pm.
- **Beds** - 8 : 2x2 (twin), 1x4 (en suite).
- **Price/night** - From £19.50pp. Twin room single occupant £23.50. Groups from £60. Camping pods from £18.50pp. Twin pod £35. Cooked breakfast £8.00. Evening meals from £12.50

CONTACT: Julie or Paul
Tel: 01857 600410
sandayhostel@gmail.com
www.ayres-rock-hostel-orkney.com
Ayre, Coo Road, Sanday,
Orkney KW17 2AY

OBSERVATORY
HOSTEL
373a

GARDIESFAULD
HOSTEL
373b

On a 34 acre croft managed by the North Ronaldsay Bird Observatory on the most northern isle of Orkney. Adjacent to a shell sand beach visited by seals and unique seaweed-eating sheep. Spectacular bird migrations and outstanding views. Ideal accommodation for those interested in wildlife but welcomes all. The hostel sleeps 10 in three dormitories with a self-catering kitchen. Lounge bar and meals available in the Observatory Guest House.

Gardiesfauld Hostel is on Unst, the most northerly of the Shetland Isles with spectacular cliffs sculpted by the Atlantic Ocean on the west and secluded, sandy beaches on the east with rocky outcrops where seals and otters appear.

On the picturesque shore at Uyeasound, this refurbished hostel has good facilities and a relaxed atmosphere. There is a kitchen, dining room, lounge, conservatory and rooms with en suite facilities as well as a garden when you can pitch a tent or park your caravan.

DETAILS
- **Open** - All year. All day. No curfews.
- **Beds** - 10: 2x4,1x2 + Guesthouse.
- **Price/night** - Hostel £18-£19.50 half board from £39.50. Guest house private rooms £58.50 - £75 half board.

CONTACT: Duty Warden
Tel: 01857 633200
nrbo@nrbo.prestel.co.uk
www.nrbo.co.uk
NRBO, North Ronaldsay, Orkney Islands, KW17 2BE

DETAILS
- **Open** - April to October. Open in winter for pre-bookings. Open all day.
- **Beds** - 35: 1x11, 2x6, 2x5, 1x2
- **Price/night** - Adults £16, U16's £9. Camping £8, U16s £4. Hook ups £18

CONTACT: Warden
Tel: 01957 755279
enquiries@gardiesfauld.shetland.co.uk
Uyeasound, Unst, Shetland, ZE2 9DW

BOOK DIRECT ON OUR WEBSITE

Every booking placed through the Independent Hostels' website is a direct booking on the hostels own website. 100% of your payment and all your communications go direct to the accommodation.

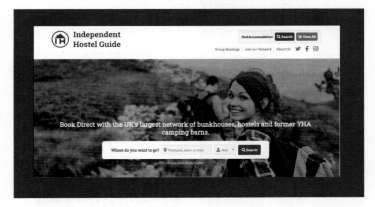

When you book with other websites they withhold up to 20% of your money as commission and often don't provide contact with your hosts until after you have booked.

BOOK DIRECT BECAUSE

Everything you pay goes to your hosts

You can chat with the staff and discuss your needs

You may get preferential treatment

On the Independent Hostels website everything you pay and everything you say goes direct to your hosts.

Be good to your hosts

BENEFITS FOR OWNERS

Support for your own marketing.

Your accommodation promoted on Facebook, Instagram & Twitter.

Direct bookings from outdoor enthusiasts, groups, families and independent travellers.

Your accommodation on our website, in this guide, in leaflets supplied to Tourist Information Centres and on the Long Distance Walkers' website.

Official **IH** Member

Independent Hostels UK

The largest network of hostels, bunkhouses & group accommodation in England, Scotland and Wales

Enquiries from all types of group leaders looking for accommodation in your area.

Your accommodation promoted at festivals and shows.

IHUK branded signs, mugs, leaflets and books.

Access to message boards sharing news from accommodation owners and emails about the latest scams and unwelcome guests.

A friendly efficient service whenever you need it.

WHO ARE INDEPENDENT HOSTELS UK ?

THE LARGEST NETWORK OF HOSTELS & BUNKHOUSES IN THE UK.

The IHUK network has a busy website and distributes guidebooks and leaflets via hostels, bookshops, tourist information centres, festivals and events.

To join IHUK visit Independenthostels.co.uk/join or phone 01629 580427

INDEX

INDEX

Carrs Farm Bunkhouse	207b
Carrshield Camping Barn	205
Castle Creavie Hay Barn ♿	309
Castle Rock Hostel	314b
Castle Ward Bunkhouse	233
Ceilidh Place Bunkhouse	362b
CellB	286a
Chapel House,The	249
Chartners Farm	220
Chatton Park Bunkhouse ♿	227a
Chellington Centre ♿	101
Chilterns Bunkhouse	102
Chitcombe Farm C.Barns	61b
Cholderton Youth Hostel ♿	72a
Cleikum Mill Lodge ♿	311
Cliffe House ♿	147
Clink261	95
Clink78 ♿	93
Clyngwyn Bunkhouse	246
Coed Owen Bunkhouse ♿	248a
Cohort Hostel	44b
Coll Bunkhouse ♿	350a
Colonsay B.packers Lodge	347b
Comrie Croft ♿	324
Conwy Valley B.packers Barn	289
Cornmill Bunkhouse	367a
Corran House	343
Corris Hostel	274
Cote Ghyll Mill	153
Court Hill Centre	103
Cragg Camping Barn	197
Cragside Bunkhouse	221
Craibstone Estate ♿	333b
Craig Y Nos Castle ♿	247
Craignure Bunkhouse ♿	346a
Croft Farm Waterpark ♿	104a
Dacres Stable C. Barn ♿	181a
Dale House Barn ♿	165
Dalehead Bunkhouse	140
Dales Bike Centre	171b
Dalesbridge,The	164
Dan Y Gyrn Bunkhouse	245
Deepdale Backpackers ♿	116b
Deepdale Groups Hostel	117
Demesne Farm Bunkhouse	215a
Deneholme ♿	209b
Denton House	192b
Derwentwater Ind. Hostel	193
Dinefwr Bunkhouse	263
Dolgoch Hostel ♿	265
Downham Camping Barn	155b
Dragons Back,The	242
Dudmaston Bunkhouse	112a
Dunfield House	106
Earby Hostel	156
Eastern Slade Barn ♿	250
Edale Barn Cotefield Farm	141a
Edens Yard Backpackers	47
Edmundbyers YHA	208
Elens Castle Hotel B.room	285a
Elmscott Hostel	50
Elterwater Hostel	183
Embassie Backpackers	148a
Euro Hostel Edinburgh Halls	313
Euro Hostel Glasgow ♿	316
Exeter Globe Backpackers	64
Exmoor Camping Barn	59
Exmoor Bunkbarn ♿	60
Exmoor Bunkhouse	56
Falmouth Lodge B.packers	46
Ffridd Bunkhouse	276b
Findhorn Village Hostel ♿	332
Fisher Gill Camping Barn	186
Florrie's Bunkhouse	212b
Fordhall Farm Bunkhouse ♿	113
Foreland Bothy	57
Forest Way Bunkhouse ♿	362a
Fort Boutique Hostel,The	150a
Fort William Backpackers	342
Foundry Adventure Centre ♿	135
Foxholes Castle B.house ♿	108b
Full Moon Backpackers	74
Galson Farm Hostel	358a
Gardiesfauld Hostel ♿	373b

INDEX